Assessment Guide

Grade 4

Houghton Mifflin Harcourt

INCLUDES:

- Prerequisite Skills Inventory
- Beginning-of-Year, Middle-of-Year, and End-of-Year Tests
- Chapter Tests
- Performance Tasks
- Getting Ready for Grade 5 Tests
- Individual Record Forms

D1209547

Printed in the U.S.A.

ISBN 978-0-544-64951-4

 7 8 9 10   0982   24 23 22 21 20

4500792918   ^ B C D E F G

Contents

Tests and Record Forms

Overview of Florida *Go Math!* Assessment

How Assessment Can Help Individualize Instruction

The *Assessment Guide* contains several types of assessment for use throughout the school year. The following pages will explain how these assessments help teachers evaluate students' understanding of the standards. This Assessment Guide also contains Individual Record Forms to help guide teachers' instructional choices and to improve students' performance.

Diagnostic Assessment

Prerequisite Skills Inventory in the *Assessment Guide* should be given at the beginning of the school year or when a new student arrives. This short-answer test assesses students' understanding of prerequisite skills. Test results provide information about the review or intervention that students may need in order to be successful in learning the mathematics related to the standards for this grade level. Suggestions for intervention are provided for this inventory.

Beginning-of-Year Test in the *Assessment Guide*, contains items that are presented in a variety of formats. This test should be given early in the year to determine which on-grade-level skills students may already understand. This benchmark test will facilitate customization of instructional content to optimize the time spent teaching specific objectives. Suggestions for intervention are provided for this test.

Show What You Know in the *Student Edition* is provided for each chapter. It assesses prior knowledge from previous grades as well as content taught earlier in the current grade. Teachers can customize instructional content using the intervention options suggested. The assessment should be scheduled at the beginning of each chapter to determine if students have the prerequisite skills for the chapter.

Formative Assessment

Lesson Quick Check in every lesson of the *Teacher Edition* monitors students' understanding of the skills and concepts being presented.

Standards Practice for every lesson in the *Standards Practice Book* helps students achieve fluency, speed, and confidence with grade level skills and concepts.

Mid-Chapter Checkpoint in the *Student Edition* provides monitoring of students' progress to permit instructional adjustments, and when required, to facilitate students' mastery of the objectives.

Middle-of-Year Test in the *Assessment Guide* assesses the same standards as the Beginning-of-Year Test, allowing students' progress to be tracked and providing opportunity for instructional adjustments, when required.

Portfolios encourage students to collect work samples throughout the chapter as a reinforcement of their progress and achievements.

Summative Assessment

Chapter Review/Tests in the *Student Edition* indicate whether additional instruction or practice is necessary for students to master the concepts and skills taught in the chapter. These tests include items presented in a variety of assessment formats.

Chapter Tests in the *Assessment Guide* evaluate students' mastery of concepts and skills taught in the chapter. These tests assess the mastery of Mathematics Florida Standards standards taught in a chapter. Item types on these tests are similar to ones a student would encounter on a test to assess Mathematics Florida Standards.

Performance Tasks in the *Assessment Guide* are provided for each Chapter and Unit. Each assessment contains several tasks to assess students' ability to use what they have learned and provides an opportunity for students to display their thinking strategies. Each set of tasks is accompanied by teacher support pages, a rubric for scoring, and examples of student work for the task.

End-of-Year Tests in the *Assessment Guide* assess the same standards as the Beginning- and Middle-of-Year Tests. It is the final benchmark test for the grade level. When students' performance on the End-of-Year Test is compared to performance on the Beginning- and Middle-of-Year Tests, teachers are able to document students' growth.

Getting Ready Tests in the *Assessment Guide* evaluate the students' understanding of concepts and skills taught as readiness for the next grade level. These tests are available in a mixed-response format comprised of multiple choice and short answer.

Data-Driven Decision Making

Go Math! allows for quick and accurate data-driven decision making so the teacher can spend more instructional time tailoring to students' needs. The **Data-Driven Decision Making** chart with Diagnostic, Formative, and Summative Assessments provides prescribed interventions so students have a greater opportunity for success with Mathematics Florida Standards.

Intervention and Review Resources

For skills that students have not yet mastered, the Reteach activities in *Reteach* or Tier 1 and Tier 2 RtI Activities online, provide additional instruction and practice on concepts and skills in the chapter.

Using Individual Record Forms

The *Assessment Guide* includes Individual Record Forms (IRF) for all tests. On these forms, each test item is correlated to the standard it assesses. There are intervention resources correlated to each item as well. A common error explains why a student may have missed the item. These forms can be used to:

- Follow progress throughout the year.
- Identify strengths, weaknesses, and provide follow-up instruction.
- Make assignments based on the intervention options provided.

Performance Assessment

Performance Assessment, together with other types of assessment, can supply the missing information not provided by other testing formats. Performance Tasks, in particular, help reveal the thinking strategies students use to work through a problem. Performance Tasks with multiple tasks for each chapter and unit are provided in the *Assessment Guide.*

Each of these assessments has several tasks that target specific math concepts, skills, and strategies. These tasks can help assess students' ability to use what they have learned to solve everyday problems. Each assessment focuses on a theme. Teachers can plan for students to complete one task at a time or use an extended amount of time to complete the entire assessment.

Teacher support pages accompany each Performance Task. A task-specific rubric helps teachers evaluate students' work. Papers to illustrate actual students' work are also provided to aid in scoring.

Portfolio Assessment

A portfolio is a collection of each student's work gathered over an extended period of time.

A portfolio illustrates the growth, talents, achievements, and reflections of the learner and provides a means for you and the student to assess performance and progress.

Building a Portfolio

There are many opportunities to collect student's work throughout the year as you use *Go Math!* Give students the opportunity to select some work samples to be included in the portfolio.

- Provide a folder for each student with the student's name clearly marked.
- Explain to students that throughout the year they will save some of their work in the folder. Sometimes it will be their individual work; sometimes it will be group reports and projects or completed checklists.

Evaluating a Portfolio

The following points made with regular portfolio evaluation will encourage growth in self-evaluation:

- Discuss the contents of the portfolio as you examine it with each student.
- Encourage and reward each student by emphasizing growth, original thinking, and completion of tasks.
- Reinforce and adjust instruction of the broad goals you want to accomplish as you evaluate the portfolios.
- Examine each portfolio on the basis of individual growth rather than in comparison with other portfolios.
- Share the portfolio with family during conferences or send the portfolio home with the student.

Assessment Formats

The assessments in the *Assessment Guide* contain item types beyond the traditional multiple-choice format. This variety allows for a more robust assessment of students' understanding of concepts. The following information is provided to help teachers familiarize students with these different types of items. An example of each item type appears on the following pages. You may want to use the examples to introduce the item types to students. The following explanations are provided to guide students in answering the questions. These pages describe the most common item types. You may find other types on some tests.

Example 1 Tell if a number rounds to a given number.

Yes or No

For this type of item, students respond to a single question with several examples. There are directions similar to, "For numbers 1a–1d, choose Yes or No to tell whether …" Tell students to be sure to answer the question for each part given below the directions. They will fill in the bubble next to "Yes" or "No" to tell whether the example fits the description in the question. They must fill in a bubble for each part.

Example 2 Answer questions about a scenario.

True or False

This type of item is similar to the Yes or No type. For the True or False items, students will see directions similar to, "For numbers 2a–2c, select True or False for each statement." Each part below the directions must be read as a stand-alone sentence. After reading the sentence, students mark True or False to indicate the answer. They need to fill in a bubble for each sentence.

Example 3 Identify examples of a property.

More Than One Correct Choice

This type of item may confuse students because it looks like a traditional multiple-choice item. Tell students this type of item will ask them to mark all that apply. Younger students may not understand what "mark all that apply" means. Tell them to carefully look at each choice and mark it if it is a correct answer.

Example 4 Circle the word that completes the sentence.

Choose From a List

Sometimes when students take a test on a computer, they will have to select a word, number, or symbol from a drop-down list. The *Go Math!* tests show a list and ask students to choose the correct answer. Tell students to make their choice by circling the correct answer. There will only be one choice that is correct.

Example 5 Sort numbers by even or odd.

Sorting

Students may be asked to sort something into categories. These items will present numbers, words, or equations on rectangular "tiles." The directions will ask students to write each of the items in the box that describes it. When the sorting involves more complex equations or drawings, each tile will have a letter next to it. Students will be asked to write the letter for the tile in the box. Tell students that sometimes they may write the same number or word in more than one box. For example, if they need to sort quadrilaterals by category, a square could be in a box labeled rectangle and another box labeled rhombus.

Example 6 Order numbers from least to greatest.

Use Given Numbers in the Answer

Students may also see numbers and symbols on tiles when they are asked to write an equation or answer a question using only numbers. They should use the given numbers to write the answer to the problem. Sometimes there will be extra numbers. They may also need to use each number more than once.

Example 7 Match related facts.

Matching

Some items will ask students to match equivalent values or other related items. The directions will specify what they should match. There will be dots to guide them in drawing lines. The matching may be between columns or rows.

Example 1

Yes or No

Fill in a bubble for each part.

For numbers 1a–1d, choose Yes or No to tell whether the number is 3,000 when it is rounded to the nearest thousand.

1a. 3,235   ○ Yes   ○ No

1b. 3,514   ○ Yes   ○ No

1c. 3,921   ○ Yes   ○ No

1d. 2,847   ○ Yes   ○ No

Example 2

True or False

Fill in a bubble for each part.

Colten has 342 pennies in his collection.
Kayla has 175 pennies in her collection.

For numbers 2a–2c, select True or False for each statement.

2a. Colten has more   ○ True   ○ False
pennies in his collection
than Kayla has.

2b. The total number of   ○ True   ○ False
pennies Colten and Kayla
have is an odd number.

2c. Kayla needs 50 more   ○ True   ○ False
pennies to have 200 pennies.

Example 3

More Than One
Correct Choice

Fill in the bubble next to all the correct answers.

Select the equations that show the Commutative Property of Addition. Mark all that apply.

Ⓐ $35 + 56 = 30 + 5 + 50 + 6$

Ⓑ $47 + 68 = 68 + 47$

Ⓒ $32 + 54 = 54 + 32$

Ⓓ $12 + 90 = 90 + 12$

Ⓔ $346 + 932 = 900 + 346 + 32$

Ⓕ $45 + 167 = 40 + 167 + 5$

Example 4

Choose From a List

Circle the word that completes the sentence.

$(25 + 17) + 23 = 25 + (17 + 23)$

The equation shows the addends in a different

order.

grouping.

operation.

Example 5

Sorting

Copy the numbers in the correct box.

Write each number in the box below the word that describes it.

| 33 | 46 | 72 | 97 |

Even	Odd

Example 6

Use Given Numbers in the Answer

Write the given numbers to answer the question.

Write the numbers in order from least to greatest.

| 345 | 267 | 390 | 714 | 873 |

_____

Example 7

Matching

Draw lines to match an item in one column to the related item in the other column.

Match the pairs of related facts.

$8 + 7 = 15$ •   • $12 - 9 = 3$

$14 - 8 = 6$ •   • $7 + 8 = 15$

$3 + 9 = 12$ •   • $9 + 7 = 16$

$16 - 7 = 9$ •   • $14 - 6 = 8$

Test Answer Sheet

1. (A) (B) (C) (D)   26. (A) (B) (C) (D)
2. (A) (B) (C) (D)   27. (A) (B) (C) (D)
3. (A) (B) (C) (D)   28. (A) (B) (C) (D)
4. (A) (B) (C) (D)   29. (A) (B) (C) (D)
5. (A) (B) (C) (D)   30. (A) (B) (C) (D)

6. (A) (B) (C) (D)   31. (A) (B) (C) (D)
7. (A) (B) (C) (D)   32. (A) (B) (C) (D)
8. (A) (B) (C) (D)   33. (A) (B) (C) (D)
9. (A) (B) (C) (D)   34. (A) (B) (C) (D)
10. (A) (B) (C) (D)   35. (A) (B) (C) (D)

11. (A) (B) (C) (D)   36. (A) (B) (C) (D)
12. (A) (B) (C) (D)   37. (A) (B) (C) (D)
13. (A) (B) (C) (D)   38. (A) (B) (C) (D)
14. (A) (B) (C) (D)   39. (A) (B) (C) (D)
15. (A) (B) (C) (D)   40. (A) (B) (C) (D)

16. (A) (B) (C) (D)   41. (A) (B) (C) (D)
17. (A) (B) (C) (D)   42. (A) (B) (C) (D)
18. (A) (B) (C) (D)   43. (A) (B) (C) (D)
19. (A) (B) (C) (D)   44. (A) (B) (C) (D)
20. (A) (B) (C) (D)   45. (A) (B) (C) (D)

21. (A) (B) (C) (D)   46. (A) (B) (C) (D)
22. (A) (B) (C) (D)   47. (A) (B) (C) (D)
23. (A) (B) (C) (D)   48. (A) (B) (C) (D)
24. (A) (B) (C) (D)   49. (A) (B) (C) (D)
25. (A) (B) (C) (D)   50. (A) (B) (C) (D)

Write the correct answer.

1. The ice skating rink rented 238 pairs of ice skates one weekend. What is 238 rounded to the nearest hundred?

_____

2. The theater has 329 fixed seats and 174 moveable seats. What could be a **reasonable estimate** of the total number of seats in the theater?

_____

3. On Saturday, the lifeguard counted 416 swimmers at the beach. On Sunday the lifeguard counted 283 swimmers at the beach. How many swimmers were at the beach in all?

_____

4. Mr. Li drove 287 miles from Hawk City to Bear Town. He then drove 175 miles from Bear Town to Cedar City. How many miles did Mr. Li drive in all?

_____

5. Hector earned 942 points in his first round of a video game. Sarah earned 791 points in her first round of the same video game. What could be a **reasonable estimate** of how many more points Hector earned than Sarah in the first round of the video game?

_____

6. Mrs. Rourke's class collected 385 cans during a recycling drive. Mr. Hardy's class collected 259 cans during the same recycling drive. How many more cans did Mrs. Rourke's class collect than Mr. Hardy's class?

_____

GO ON ➡

7. Campers go to Ridgeline Camp for one week sessions. During the first week of camp, there were 112 campers. During the second week, there were 15 fewer campers than in the first week. How many campers were at camp during both weeks?

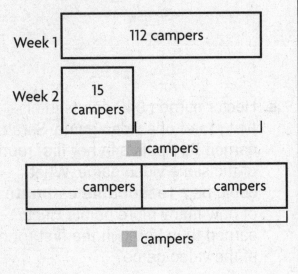

| Week 1 | 112 campers |

| Week 2 | 15 campers |

_____ campers

| _____ campers | _____ campers |

_____ campers

_____

8. A seamstress measured the lengths of several ribbons. She recorded the data in the line plot below.

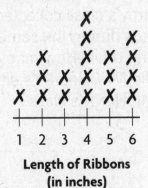

Length of Ribbons
(in inches)

How many ribbons are 5 inches long?

_____

9. Kevin divided his model airplane collection into 3 groups. Each group has 5 airplanes.

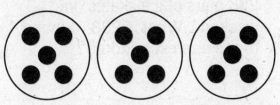

How many model airplanes does Kevin have in his collection?

_____

10. There are 4 jars for markers in Maya's class. Maya found 0 markers in each jar. Write a number sentence that shows how many markers Maya found in all.

_____

11. Mrs. Murphy bought 2 boxes of granola bars. Each box has 6 bars. How many granola bars did Mrs. Murphy buy in all?

_____

Name _____

12. Wendy writes a pattern of numbers.

21, 28, 35, 42, 49

How can you describe this pattern?

_____

13. Find a pattern used in the table.
Then complete the table.

Necklaces	2	3	4	5	6
Beads	18	27	36		

_____

14. Sam plans to buy 24 slices of pizza
for a party. There are 8 slices in
each whole pizza. How many pizzas
does Sam need to buy?

$$p \times 8 = 24$$

_____

15. One pack of construction paper
has 40 sheets of paper. How many
sheets are in 6 packs?

_____

16. Omar writes a set of related facts.
One of the facts he writes is
$30 \div 5 = 6$. Write an equation
that is included in the same set of
related facts.

_____

_____

17. Melody brought 5 bones to the dog
park. She gave an equal number
of bones to each of 5 dogs. How
many bones did Melody give to
each dog?

_____

18. Simone wants to put 10 photos
on each page of her scrap book.
She has picked out 70 photos she
wants to use. How many scrap
book pages does Simone use?

_____

19. A school lunch table seats
6 students. How many lunch tables
are needed to seat 18 students?

_____

GO ON ▶

20. Brad's little brother has a storage box for his toy cars. Each section of the box holds 8 toy cars. How many sections does the box have if it holds 56 cars?

_____

21. Ryan arranged 40 blocks in 8 equal rows. How many blocks are in each row?

_____

22. Susie separates 18 stickers into 9 equal groups. How many stickers are in each group?

_____

23. Luke needs to divide a sheet of paper into two equal parts. Draw a line to divide the square into 2 equal parts.

24. Toni made a model to show the number of students on the playground. The shaded part of the model shows the fraction of students on the slide.

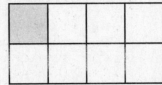

What fraction of students are on the slide?

_____

25. A student shaded this model. The shaded part shows what part of the pottery glazes in the art room have glitter in them.

What fraction of the pottery glazes have glitter?

_____

26. Mrs. Parker bought $\frac{3}{4}$ pound of strawberries and $\frac{1}{4}$ pound of raspberries. Write a statement to compare the amounts of berries.

_____

GO ON

27. Of all the students in Matea's class, $\frac{2}{3}$ are wearing sneakers and $\frac{2}{6}$ are wearing sandals. What symbol compares the fractions correctly? Write $<$, $>$, or $=$.

$$\frac{2}{3} \bigcirc \frac{2}{6}$$

28. A scientist measures the lengths of three beetles. The first beetle is $\frac{4}{8}$ inch long. The second beetle is $\frac{2}{8}$ inch long. The third beetle is $\frac{7}{8}$ inch long. Write the fractions in order from **least** to **greatest**.

_____

29. Hannah is selling slices of pie at the bake sale. The pie has 8 slices. She has sold $\frac{1}{4}$ of the slices.

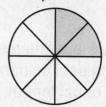

What fraction with a denominator of 8 is equal to $\frac{1}{4}$?

_____

30. Jake looked at the clock before leaving for school. The hour hand was between the 7 and the 8. The minute hand was on the 9. What time did Jake leave for school?

_____

31. Ling started running at 10:18 A.M. She finished running at 10:50 A.M. How long did Ling run?

_____

32. A batch of muffins needs to bake in the oven for 24 minutes. Scott puts the muffins in the oven at 2:17 P.M. What time will he take the muffins out of the oven?

_____

33. Latonya fills a drinking glass with water. Write *more than 1 liter*, *about 1 liter*, or *less than 1 liter* to estimate how much water the glass will hold.

_____

GO ON

34. Julia wants to find the mass of her textbooks. Write *grams* or *kilograms* to name the **best** unit to use to find the mass of the textbooks.

_____

35. Jillian uses a balance to compare the masses of the objects shown. Use the words *is less than*, *is the same*, or *is more than* to compare the masses of the objects.

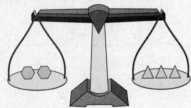

_____

36. How many right angles does this shape appear to have?

_____

37. Carrie drew this shape. Use *right angle*, *less than a right angle*, or *greater than a right angle* to describe the marked angle.

_____

38. Hank used line segments to draw a shape. Look at the bold sides of his shape.

Write *intersecting*, *perpendicular*, or *parallel* to describe the sides.

_____

39. Blake drew this shape.

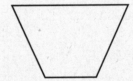

Name Blake's quadrilateral.

_____

40. Lisa drew a quadrilateral with 4 right angles. The parallel sides are equal length. Which quadrilateral best describes her drawing?

_____

STOP

Name _____

Choose the correct answer.

1. Daniel plans to use a strategy to find 18 × 470. Which expression shows a strategy he could use?

   (A) 4 × 5 × 470

   (B) 3 × 6 × 470

   (C) 6 × 3 × 47

   (D) 18 × 0 × 470

2. Mia has 2,590 digital photos saved on her computer. Ella has 5 times as many saved on her computer. How many digital photos does Ella have saved on her computer?

   (A) 12,950

   (B) 12,550

   (C) 11,550

   (D) 10,950

3. A factory can make 2,035 markers in one hour. Which is the **best** estimate of how many markers can be made in 6 hours?

   (A) 1,200 markers

   (B) 2,000 markers

   (C) 12,000 markers

   (D) 20,000 markers

4. Ryan made this model to find the product of a 3-digit number and a 1-digit number.

   What multiplication sentence represents Ryan's model?

   (A) 5 × 264 = 1,320

   (B) 5 × 260 = 1,300

   (C) 5 × 246 = 1,230

   (D) 5 × 204 = 1,020

5. Kate lives 0.6 mile from her school. Which fraction is equivalent to 0.6?

   (A) $\frac{0}{6}$

   (B) $\frac{6}{100}$

   (C) $\frac{1}{6}$

   (D) $\frac{6}{10}$

GO ON

6. Anna jogged $1\frac{3}{10}$ miles on a path in the park. What is this distance written as a decimal?

Ⓐ 0.13 mile

Ⓑ 1.03 miles

Ⓒ 1.3 miles

Ⓓ 13 miles

7. Rico walked for $\frac{3}{10}$ mile. Then he walked for $\frac{24}{100}$ mile. How far did he walk in all?

Ⓐ $\frac{54}{100}$ mile

Ⓑ $\frac{5}{10}$ mile

Ⓒ $\frac{30}{100}$ mile

Ⓓ $\frac{27}{100}$ mile

8. What is the measure of the unknown angle in the figure?

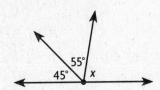

Ⓐ 180°

Ⓑ 100°

Ⓒ 80°

Ⓓ 70°

9. David drew the angle below.

35°

What name should David give his angle?

Ⓐ obtuse angle

Ⓑ acute angle

Ⓒ right angle

Ⓓ straight angle

10. Maria put two angles together to form a straight angle. One angle measures 112°. What is the measure of the other angle?

Ⓐ 78°

Ⓑ 68°

Ⓒ 58°

Ⓓ 48°

GO ON

Name _____

11. How many degrees are in an angle that turns through $\frac{1}{2}$ of a circle?

Ⓐ 90°

Ⓑ 180°

Ⓒ 270°

Ⓓ 360°

12. Flora needs $\frac{3}{8}$ yard of blue ribbon and $\frac{2}{8}$ yard of red ribbon to make a bow for a present she is wrapping. How much ribbon does Flora need in all?

Ⓐ $\frac{1}{8}$ yard

Ⓑ $\frac{5}{16}$ yard

Ⓒ $\frac{5}{8}$ yard

Ⓓ $\frac{7}{8}$ yard

13. Tyler brought $\frac{7}{12}$ pound of trail mix on a camping trip. He ate $\frac{4}{12}$ pound of the trail mix. How much trail mix is left?

Ⓐ $\frac{11}{12}$ pound

Ⓑ $\frac{4}{12}$ pound

Ⓒ $\frac{3}{12}$ pound

Ⓓ $\frac{1}{12}$ pound

14. Mark rode his bike $\frac{22}{8}$ miles. Which mixed number shows the fraction of miles he rode his bike?

Ⓐ $2\frac{6}{8}$ miles

Ⓑ $2\frac{4}{8}$ miles

Ⓒ $2\frac{3}{8}$ miles

Ⓓ $2\frac{1}{8}$ miles

15. Zoey has $8\frac{1}{3}$ feet of blue yarn and $4\frac{2}{3}$ feet of green yarn. How much more blue yarn does Zoey have than green yarn?

Ⓐ $3\frac{1}{3}$ feet

Ⓑ $3\frac{2}{3}$ feet

Ⓒ $4\frac{1}{3}$ feet

Ⓓ $4\frac{2}{3}$ feet

GO ON

16. Kayla has 36 flower stickers, 27 bird stickers, and 18 butterfly stickers. She wants to put an equal number of each type of sticker into bags so all of the bags will be the same. How many of each kind of sticker can Kayla put in each bag?

(A) 9

(B) 1 or 9

(C) 1, 3, or 9

(D) 1, 3, 9, 12, or 18

17. Leah and Tony were playing a game. Leah was counting by 8s. Tony was counting by 3s. They paced the counting so they would say the first common number together. What is the first number they both said together?

(A) 12

(B) 24

(C) 32

(D) 36

18. Chen's friend Bob is helping him learn about prime numbers. Bob writes a list of numbers and asks Chen to choose the prime number. Which number should Chen choose?

(A) 12

(B) 24

(C) 31

(D) 36

19. Liz and Dave made a secret code. They wrote some numbers in the code to help them remember the pattern.

8, 11, 10, 13, 12, 15, 14, 17

What should be the next number in the code?

(A) 15

(B) 16

(C) 18

(D) 20

20. The Simmons family is taking a 2-week vacation to Alaska. How many days will their vacation last?

(A) 7 days

(B) 14 days

(C) 21 days

(D) 24 days

GO ON

21. The table shows a pattern for two units of customary length.

_____	_____
1	12
2	24
3	36
4	48

Which are the best labels for each column?

Ⓐ Miles, Yards

Ⓑ Yards, Feet

Ⓒ Yards, Inches

Ⓓ Feet, Inches

22. The tour of the space museum started at 10:45 A.M. It lasted for 1 hour 30 minutes. What time did the tour end?

Ⓐ 11:15 A.M.

Ⓑ 11:45 P.M.

Ⓒ 12:15 P.M.

Ⓓ 1:15 P.M.

23. Patrick mixed 3 quarts 1 pint of orange juice with 3 pints of cranberry juice and 1 pint of grape juice to make punch. How much punch does he have?

Ⓐ 5 quarts 1 pint

Ⓑ 5 quarts

Ⓒ 4 quarts 1 pint

Ⓓ 4 quarts

24. Karen scored 157,834 points on the third level of her computer game. What is the value of the digit 5 in 157,834?

Ⓐ 500,000

Ⓑ 50,000

Ⓒ 5,000

Ⓓ 500

25. Maria used number tiles to make the number 538,397. Jimmy used number tiles to make the number 583,397. Which statement about these numbers is correct?

Ⓐ 583,397 < 538,397

Ⓑ 583,397 > 538,397

Ⓒ 583,397 = 538,397

Ⓓ 538,397 > 583,397

GO ON

26. Pete's Pizza sold 65,182 pizzas the first year they were open. They sold 58,458 pizzas the second year. What was the total number of pizzas sold during the first two years of business?

(A) 113,640

(B) 123,540

(C) 123,630

(D) 123,640

27. The town Sean lives in has 48,968 people. The town Debra lives in has 73,815 people. How many more people live in Debra's town?

(A) 24,847

(B) 24,947

(C) 25,847

(D) 34,847

28. Patel uses 150 feet of fencing to fence in his rectangular garden. The width of the garden is 25 feet. What is the length of the garden?

(A) 65 feet

(B) 40 feet

(C) 50 feet

(D) 60 feet

29. Molly builds a rectangular exercise pen for her hamsters.

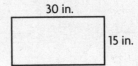

What is the perimeter of the exercise pen?

(A) 45 inches

(B) 90 inches

(C) 100 inches

(D) 450 inches

30. Mr. Wilson is building a new patio off the back of his house.

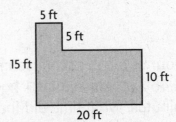

How much tile does Mr. Wilson need to cover his patio?

(A) 60 square feet

(B) 200 square feet

(C) 225 square feet

(D) 275 square feet

GO ON

31. One wall of Eric's bedroom is 15 feet wide and 8 feet high. A door on the wall is 7 feet high and 3 feet wide. How much wall paper will Eric need to cover the wall?

- (A) 120 square feet
- (B) 110 square feet
- (C) 99 square feet
- (D) 89 square feet

32. Which shows the **best** estimate to use to find 43×28?

- (A) $40 \times 20 = 800$
- (B) $45 \times 20 = 900$
- (C) $40 \times 30 = 1,200$
- (D) $50 \times 30 = 1,500$

33. Sofia can text 40 words in one minute. At that rate, how many words can she text in 12 minutes?

- (A) 400
- (B) 480
- (C) 580
- (D) 720

34. From noon to 1 P.M., customers bought 85 pizzas at $18 each. What is the total amount customers paid for the pizzas?

- (A) $1,430
- (B) $1,490
- (C) $1,530
- (D) $1,620

35. Use comparative relational thinking to find the unknown number.

$87 - n = 92 - 18$

- (A) $n = 13$
- (B) $n = 23$
- (C) $n = 74$
- (D) $n = 161$

GO ON

36. Yoshi says he needs a board that is $\frac{17}{4}$ feet long. How can Yoshi rename the fraction as a mixed number?

Ⓐ $5\frac{1}{4}$

Ⓑ $4\frac{1}{4}$

Ⓒ $3\frac{1}{4}$

Ⓓ $2\frac{1}{4}$

37. Marsha named a fraction that was **not** a multiple of $\frac{3}{6}$. Which fraction could she have named?

Ⓐ $\frac{6}{6}$

Ⓑ $\frac{9}{6}$

Ⓒ $\frac{11}{6}$

Ⓓ $\frac{15}{6}$

38. Carlos lives $\frac{3}{8}$ mile from his school. He walks to school each morning and gets a ride home after school. How far does Carlos walk to school in 5 days?

Ⓐ 1 mile

Ⓑ $1\frac{3}{4}$ miles

Ⓒ $1\frac{7}{8}$ miles

Ⓓ $2\frac{7}{8}$ miles

39. Maya spent $1\frac{1}{6}$ hours a day working on her science project. It took her 4 days to complete the project. How much time in all did it take Maya to complete her science project?

Ⓐ $4\frac{4}{6}$ hours

Ⓑ $4\frac{1}{6}$ hours

Ⓒ $3\frac{4}{6}$ hours

Ⓓ $3\frac{1}{6}$ hours

40. On Friday, 148 fourth graders went on a field trip to a wildlife park. The staff divided them into 5 tour groups. Which is the **best** estimate of the number of students in each group?

Ⓐ 50

Ⓑ 40

Ⓒ 30

Ⓓ 20

GO ON

Name _____

41. Steven needs 42 stickers to decorate a poster he is making. The stickers come on sheets of 12. What is the least number of sheets of stickers Steven should buy?

Ⓐ 5

Ⓑ 4

Ⓒ 3

Ⓓ 2

42. A store gave away 1,498 calendars in 7 days. They gave away the same number of calendars each day. How many calendars did the store give away each day?

Ⓐ 21

Ⓑ 204

Ⓒ 214

Ⓓ 224

43. A cookie factory packs 6 small cookies in a sample pack. The factory gives the sample packs to visitors. How many sample packs can they make with 1,800 cookies?

Ⓐ 3,000

Ⓑ 300

Ⓒ 30

Ⓓ 3

44. Jared drew the figure below.

How many lines of symmetry does the figure have?

Ⓐ 4

Ⓑ 3

Ⓒ 2

Ⓓ 1

45. Bella drew the figure below as an example for her classmate.

Which of the following terms **best** describes the figure Bella drew?

Ⓐ line segment

Ⓑ line

Ⓒ angle

Ⓓ ray

GO ON

46. The garden in Juan's backyard is in the shape of a trapezoid with only 1 pair of parallel sides. Which figure could be the shape of Juan's garden?

Ⓐ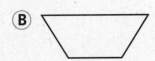

Ⓑ

Ⓒ

Ⓓ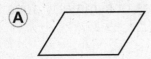

47. A sign is in the shape of an obtuse triangle. Which of the following could be the shape of the sign?

Ⓐ

Ⓑ

Ⓒ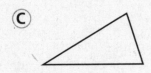

Ⓓ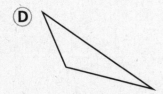

48. Luisa ran $\frac{3}{5}$ mile yesterday and $\frac{1}{2}$ mile today. Which number is a common denominator for $\frac{3}{5}$ and $\frac{1}{2}$?

Ⓐ 12

Ⓑ 10

Ⓒ 5

Ⓓ 2

49. Justin needs $\frac{2}{3}$ quart of orange juice for the drink he is making. Which fraction is equivalent to $\frac{2}{3}$?

Ⓐ $\frac{4}{9}$

Ⓑ $\frac{1}{2}$

Ⓒ $\frac{6}{9}$

Ⓓ $\frac{4}{3}$

50. Jasmine cut $\frac{3}{8}$ yard of blue ribbon and $\frac{1}{3}$ yard of red ribbon to decorate a package. Which statement correctly compares the fractions?

Ⓐ $\frac{1}{3} > \frac{3}{8}$

Ⓑ $\frac{1}{3} = \frac{3}{8}$

Ⓒ $\frac{3}{8} > \frac{1}{3}$

Ⓓ $\frac{3}{8} < \frac{1}{3}$

STOP

Choose the correct answer.

1. John plans to use a strategy to find 32×120. Which expression shows a strategy he could use?

   Ⓐ $4 \times 8 \times 120$

   Ⓑ $4 \times 8 \times 12$

   Ⓒ $8 \times 4 \times 100$

   Ⓓ $32 \times 0 \times 120$

2. Ava took 3,454 digital photos last year. Emily took 4 times as many. How many digital photos did Emily take last year?

   Ⓐ 12,816

   Ⓑ 13,616

   Ⓒ 13,806

   Ⓓ 13,816

3. A factory can produce 3,120 cars in a week. Which is the **best** estimate of how many cars the factory can produce in 4 weeks?

   Ⓐ 1,200

   Ⓑ 2,000

   Ⓒ 12,000

   Ⓓ 20,000

4. Ethan made this model to find the product of a 3-digit number and a 1-digit number.

	400	30	8
6			

   What multiplication sentence represents Ethan's model?

   Ⓐ $6 \times 483 = 2{,}898$

   Ⓑ $6 \times 438 = 2{,}628$

   Ⓒ $6 \times 430 = 2{,}580$

   Ⓓ $6 \times 408 = 2{,}448$

5. Anna lives 0.8 mile from the mall. Which fraction is equivalent to 0.8?

   Ⓐ $\frac{0}{8}$

   Ⓑ $\frac{1}{8}$

   Ⓒ $\frac{8}{10}$

   Ⓓ $\frac{8}{100}$

GO ON ▶

Name _____

6. Jack jogged $2\frac{5}{10}$ miles on a path in the park. What is this distance written as a decimal?

　Ⓐ 0.25 mile

　Ⓑ 2.5 miles

　Ⓒ 5.2 miles

　Ⓓ 25 miles

7. Roberto walked for $\frac{6}{10}$ miles. Then he walked for $\frac{25}{100}$ miles. How far did he walk in all?

　Ⓐ $\frac{31}{100}$ mile

　Ⓑ $\frac{35}{100}$ mile

　Ⓒ $\frac{85}{100}$ mile

　Ⓓ $\frac{95}{100}$ mile

8. What is the measure of the unknown angle in the figure?

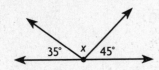

　Ⓐ 180°

　Ⓑ 100°

　Ⓒ 90°

　Ⓓ 80°

9. Melanie drew the angle below.

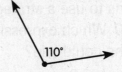

What name should Melanie give her angle?

　Ⓐ obtuse angle

　Ⓑ acute angle

　Ⓒ right angle

　Ⓓ straight angle

10. Miko put two angles together to form a straight angle. One angle measures 88°. What is the measure of the other angle?

　Ⓐ 92°

　Ⓑ 82°

　Ⓒ 72°

　Ⓓ 42°

GO ON

11. How many degrees are in an angle that turns through $\frac{1}{4}$ of a circle?

Ⓐ 360°

Ⓑ 270°

Ⓒ 180°

Ⓓ 90°

12. Rosa needs $\frac{5}{12}$ yard of blue ribbon and $\frac{6}{12}$ yard of yellow ribbon to trim a banner she is making. How much ribbon does Rosa need in all?

Ⓐ $\frac{11}{12}$ yard

Ⓑ $\frac{3}{4}$ yard

Ⓒ $\frac{1}{2}$ yard

Ⓓ $\frac{11}{24}$ yard

13. Sam brought $\frac{7}{8}$ pound of trail mix on a camping trip. He ate $\frac{4}{8}$ pound of the trail mix. How much trail mix is left?

Ⓐ $\frac{11}{8}$ pound

Ⓑ $\frac{1}{2}$ pound

Ⓒ $\frac{3}{8}$ pound

Ⓓ $\frac{1}{8}$ pound

14. Ryan rode his bike $\frac{18}{4}$ miles. Which mixed number shows the fraction of miles he rode his bike?

Ⓐ $4\frac{3}{4}$ miles

Ⓑ $4\frac{2}{4}$ miles

Ⓒ $4\frac{1}{4}$ miles

Ⓓ $4\frac{1}{8}$ miles

15. Sarah has $6\frac{2}{4}$ meters of rope and $3\frac{3}{4}$ meters of string. How much more rope does Sarah have than string?

Ⓐ 3 meters

Ⓑ $2\frac{3}{4}$ meters

Ⓒ $2\frac{1}{2}$ meters

Ⓓ $2\frac{1}{4}$ meters

GO ON

16. Maya has 28 apples, 12 oranges, and 8 mangos. She wants to put an equal number of each kind of fruit into baskets so all of the baskets will be the same. How many of each kind of fruit can Maya put in each basket?

(A) 4

(B) 1, 2 or 4

(C) 1 or 4

(D) 1, 3, 4, 6, or 8

17. Molly and Brian are playing a game. Molly is counting by 8s. Brian is counting by 6s. They pace the counting so they will say the first common number together. What is the first number they both say together?

(A) 12

(B) 18

(C) 24

(D) 32

18. Eric's friend Hiroshi is helping him learn about prime numbers. Hiroshi writes down a list of numbers and asks Eric to choose the prime number. Which number should Eric choose?

(A) 8

(B) 11

(C) 16

(D) 32

19. Don texts a number pattern to his friend Lou.

4, 8, 6, 10, 8, 12, 10, 14

Lou texts the next number in the pattern back to Don. What is the number?

(A) 18

(B) 15

(C) 12

(D) 10

20. Mark's family has lived in the same town for 3 years. How many months have they lived in the town?

(A) 36 months

(B) 32 months

(C) 30 months

(D) 24 months

GO ON

21. The table shows a pattern for two units of customary weight.

_____	_____
1	16
2	32
3	48
4	64

Which are the best labels for each column?

Ⓐ Yards, Feet

Ⓑ Kilograms, Grams

Ⓒ Tons, Pounds

Ⓓ Pounds, Ounces

22. The bus left for the nature center at 9:15 A.M. The trip there took 1 hour 45 minutes. What time did the bus arrive at the nature center?

Ⓐ 11:00 A.M.

Ⓑ 10:45 A.M.

Ⓒ 10:15 A.M.

Ⓓ 10:00 A.M.

23. Pedro mixed 1 pound 6 ounces of apples with 1 pound 4 ounces of oranges and 12 ounces of strawberries to make a fruit salad. How much fruit salad does he have?

Ⓐ 3 pounds 6 ounces

Ⓑ 3 pounds 4 ounces

Ⓒ 3 pounds

Ⓓ 2 pounds 6 ounces

24. Kevin's brother got 738,256 hits on his new website. What is the value of the digit 7 in 738,256?

Ⓐ 7,000

Ⓑ 70,000

Ⓒ 700,000

Ⓓ 7,000,000

25. Tina used number tiles to make the number 327,869. Jeremy used number tiles to make the number 327,689. Which statement about these numbers is correct?

Ⓐ 327,689 > 327,869

Ⓑ 327,689 < 327,869

Ⓒ 327,689 = 327,869

Ⓓ 327,869 < 327,689

GO ON ➡

26. Paul got a new video game. He scored 35,698 points on his first game and 48,735 points on his second game. What was the total number of points for both games?

Ⓐ 84,433

Ⓑ 84,423

Ⓒ 84,333

Ⓓ 74,433

27. The city Laura lives in has 56,759 people living in it. The city Jeff lives in has 82,458 people living in it. How many more people live in Jeff's city?

Ⓐ 35,699

Ⓑ 25,789

Ⓒ 25,699

Ⓓ 25,409

28. The public pool Brent goes to has a perimeter of 270 feet. The width of the pool is 45 feet. What is the length of the rectangular pool?

Ⓐ 225 feet

Ⓑ 180 feet

Ⓒ 90 feet

Ⓓ 6 feet

29. Elaine builds a rectangular flower box to put on her family's porch.

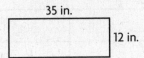

What is the perimeter of the flower box?

Ⓐ 47 inches

Ⓑ 82 inches

Ⓒ 94 inches

Ⓓ 420 inches

30. Mr. Lee drew these plans for a new garden in his backyard.

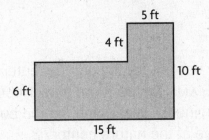

What will the area of Mr. Lee's garden be?

Ⓐ 150 square feet

Ⓑ 110 square feet

Ⓒ 90 square feet

Ⓓ 40 square feet

GO ON

31. Joseph's notebook cover is 12 inches by 8 inches. He put a wildlife sticker on the notebook. If the sticker is 3 inches by 2 inches. How much of the notebook cover is still showing?

(A) 108 square inches

(B) 96 square inches

(C) 90 square inches

(D) 84 square inches

32. Which shows the **best** estimate to use to find 18×62?

(A) $20 \times 70 = 1,400$

(B) $20 \times 60 = 1,200$

(C) $20 \times 50 = 1,000$

(D) $10 \times 70 = 700$

33. Miko can type 70 words in one minute. At that rate, how many words can she type in 12 minutes?

(A) 800

(B) 820

(C) 840

(D) 880

34. Between noon and 1 P.M., customers bought 76 CDs at $16 each. What is the total amount customers paid for the CDs?

(A) $1,216

(B) $1,186

(C) $1,116

(D) $532

35. Use comparative relational thinking to find the unknown number.

$54 + 17 = 62 + n$

(A) $n = 8$

(B) $n = 9$

(C) $n = 71$

(D) $n = 133$

GO ON

36. Megan says she needs a piece of rope that is $\frac{15}{6}$ feet long. How can Megan rename the fraction as a mixed number?

Ⓐ $3\frac{3}{6}$

Ⓑ $2\frac{3}{6}$

Ⓒ $2\frac{1}{3}$

Ⓓ $1\frac{3}{6}$

37. Carla named a fraction that was **not** a multiple of $\frac{3}{8}$. Which fraction could she have named?

Ⓐ $\frac{6}{8}$

Ⓑ $\frac{9}{8}$

Ⓒ $\frac{12}{8}$

Ⓓ $\frac{14}{8}$

38. Marko runs $\frac{3}{5}$ mile 3 times a week. How far does Marko run each week?

Ⓐ $3\frac{3}{5}$ miles

Ⓑ $2\frac{2}{5}$ miles

Ⓒ $1\frac{4}{5}$ miles

Ⓓ $1\frac{3}{5}$ miles

39. Ruby spends $1\frac{1}{4}$ hours a day practicing the piano. She practices 6 days a week. How much time in all does Ruby spend practicing the piano each week?

Ⓐ $8\frac{1}{2}$ hours

Ⓑ $7\frac{1}{2}$ hours

Ⓒ $7\frac{1}{4}$ hours

Ⓓ $6\frac{1}{4}$ hours

40. On Friday, 142 fourth graders went on a field trip to an aquarium. The staff divided them into 7 tour groups. Which is the **best** estimate of the number of students in each group?

Ⓐ 50

Ⓑ 40

Ⓒ 30

Ⓓ 20

GO ON

41. Jared needs 54 balloons to decorate a room for a birthday party. The balloons come in packages of 20. What is the smallest number of packages of balloons Jared should buy?

(A) 5

(B) 4

(C) 3

(D) 2

42. A new pet store handed out 2,472 coupons in 4 days. They handed out the same number of coupons each day. How many coupons did the store hand out each day?

(A) 61

(B) 518

(C) 608

(D) 618

43. A sock factory packs 5 pairs of socks to a package. How many packages can they pack with 3,000 pairs of socks?

(A) 6 packages

(B) 60 packages

(C) 600 packages

(D) 6,000 packages

44. Andrew drew the figure below.

How many lines of symmetry does the figure have?

(A) 4

(B) 3

(C) 2

(D) 1

45. Julie drew the figure below as an example for her classmate.

Which of the following terms **best** describes the figure Julie drew?

(A) line segment

(B) line

(C) angle

(D) ray

GO ON

46. A fishpond is in the shape of a rhombus. Which figure could be the shape of the fishpond?

Ⓐ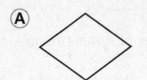

Ⓑ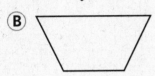

Ⓒ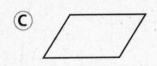

Ⓓ

47. A sign is in the shape of an acute triangle. Which of the following could be the shape of the sign?

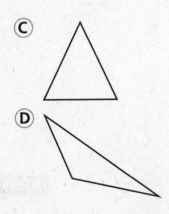

48. Jing read $\frac{1}{2}$ of his book on Saturday and $\frac{2}{3}$ of his book on Sunday. Which number is a common denominator for $\frac{1}{2}$ and $\frac{2}{3}$?

Ⓐ 1

Ⓑ 4

Ⓒ 6

Ⓓ 10

49. Tami needs $\frac{3}{4}$ gallon of paint. Which fraction is equivalent to $\frac{3}{4}$?

Ⓐ $\frac{3}{16}$

Ⓑ $\frac{9}{16}$

Ⓒ $\frac{9}{12}$

Ⓓ $\frac{6}{4}$

50. Nori bought $\frac{2}{3}$ pound of chicken salad and $\frac{3}{4}$ pound of tuna salad for a picnic. Which statement correctly compares the fractions?

Ⓐ $\frac{2}{3} > \frac{3}{4}$

Ⓑ $\frac{3}{4} > \frac{2}{3}$

Ⓒ $\frac{2}{3} = \frac{3}{4}$

Ⓓ $\frac{3}{4} < \frac{2}{3}$

STOP

Choose the correct answer.

1. Juan plans to use a strategy to find
   12 × 380. Which expression shows a
   strategy he could use?

   Ⓐ 3 × 4 × 38

   Ⓑ 4 × 4 × 380

   Ⓒ 12 × 0 × 380

   Ⓓ 3 × 4 × 380

2. Kate's family saved 2,573 pennies last
   year. Zoe's family saved 3 times as
   many. How many pennies did Zoe's
   family save last year?

   Ⓐ 8,519

   Ⓑ 7,729

   Ⓒ 7,719

   Ⓓ 7,519

3. A factory can make 3,848 pencils in
   one hour. Which is the **best** estimate
   of how many pencils can be made in
   4 hours?

   Ⓐ 160,000 pencils

   Ⓑ 16,000 pencils

   Ⓒ 12,000 pencils

   Ⓓ 1,600 markers

4. Mario made this model to find the
   product of a 3-digit number and a
   1-digit number

   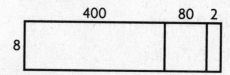

   What multiplication sentence
   represents Mario's model?

   Ⓐ 8 × 402 = 3,216

   Ⓑ 8 × 428 = 3,424

   Ⓒ 8 × 480 = 3,840

   Ⓓ 8 × 482 = 3,856

5. Julia lives 0.3 mile from the park.
   Which fraction is equivalent to 0.3?

   Ⓐ $\frac{1}{3}$

   Ⓑ $\frac{3}{10}$

   Ⓒ $\frac{3}{100}$

   Ⓓ $\frac{0}{3}$

GO ON ➡

Name _____

6. Tony rode his bicycle $3\frac{7}{10}$ miles to school. What is this distance written as a decimal?

Ⓐ 0.037 mile

Ⓑ 0.37 mile

Ⓒ 3.7 miles

Ⓓ 37 miles

7. Craig hiked for $\frac{7}{10}$ mile and stopped to take pictures. Then he hiked for another $\frac{25}{100}$ mile. How far did he hike in all?

Ⓐ $\frac{32}{100}$ mile

Ⓑ $\frac{70}{100}$ mile

Ⓒ $\frac{85}{100}$ mile

Ⓓ $\frac{95}{100}$ mile

8. What is the measure of the unknown angle in the figure?

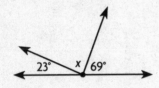

Ⓐ 180°

Ⓑ 92°

Ⓒ 88°

Ⓓ 44°

9. Caroline drew the angle below.

90°

What name should Caroline give her angle?

Ⓐ obtuse angle

Ⓑ acute angle

Ⓒ right angle

Ⓓ straight angle

10. Eric put two angles together to form a straight angle. One angle measures 115°. What is the measure of the other angle?

Ⓐ 65°

Ⓑ 75°

Ⓒ 85°

Ⓓ 95°

GO ON

11. How many degrees are in an angle that turns through $\frac{1}{3}$ of a circle?

Ⓐ 360°

Ⓑ 180°

Ⓒ 120°

Ⓓ 90°

12. Irene bought $\frac{9}{16}$ pound of wheat flour and $\frac{4}{16}$ pound of rye flour to use in a bread recipe. How much flour did Irene buy in all?

Ⓐ $\frac{15}{16}$ pound

Ⓑ $\frac{13}{16}$ pound

Ⓒ $\frac{1}{2}$ pound

Ⓓ $\frac{13}{32}$ pound

13. Dan has a piece of wood that is $\frac{9}{10}$ meter long. He uses $\frac{6}{10}$ meter of the piece of wood for a model boat he is building. How much of the piece of wood does Dan have left?

Ⓐ $\frac{15}{10}$ meters

Ⓑ $\frac{3}{5}$ meter

Ⓒ $\frac{5}{10}$ meter

Ⓓ $\frac{3}{10}$ meter

14. One of the hiking trails at a state park is $\frac{14}{3}$ miles long. Which mixed number shows the length of the hiking trail?

Ⓐ $4\frac{2}{3}$ miles

Ⓑ $4\frac{1}{3}$ miles

Ⓒ $3\frac{2}{3}$ miles

Ⓓ $3\frac{1}{3}$ miles

15. Emma has $5\frac{3}{8}$ pounds of potato salad and $2\frac{7}{8}$ pounds of egg salad for a picnic. How many more pounds of potato salad than egg salad does Emma have?

Ⓐ 3 pounds

Ⓑ $2\frac{3}{4}$ pounds

Ⓒ $2\frac{1}{2}$ pounds

Ⓓ $2\frac{1}{4}$ pounds

GO ON

16. Anna has 32 red beads, 16 blue beads, and 8 green beads. She wants to put an equal number of each kind of bead on necklaces she is making. How many of each kind of bead can Anna put on each necklace?

(A) 8

(B) 2, 4 or 8

(C) 2 or 4

(D) 1, 2, 4, or 8

17. Paula and Karen are playing a game. Paula counts by 4s. Karen counts by 5s. They try to pace the counting so they will say the first common number together. What is the first number they both say together?

(A) 20

(B) 15

(C) 12

(D) 5

18. Jeff's teacher writes a list of numbers on the board. She asks Jeff to circle the prime number. Which number should Jeff circle?

(A) 6

(B) 10

(C) 13

(D) 15

19. Ming writes a number pattern on a slip of paper and hands it to his friend Jack.

24, 21, 23, 20, 22, 19, 21, 18

Jack writes the next number in the pattern and hands the paper back to Ming. What number should Jack write?

(A) 19

(B) 20

(C) 21

(D) 22

20. Dawn's family is taking a 3-day vacation to visit her cousins. How many hours will they be away?

(A) 24 hours

(B) 36 hours

(C) 48 hours

(D) 72 hours

GO ON

21. The table shows a pattern for two units of customary capacity.

_____	_____
1	4
2	8
3	12
4	16

Which are the best labels for each column?

Ⓐ Gallons, Cups

Ⓑ Quarts, Cups

Ⓒ Pints, Cups

Ⓓ Cups, Fluid Ounces

22. Carlos and his family left for the amusement park at 8:35 A.M. The trip took 1 hour 55 minutes. What time did they arrive?

Ⓐ 9.35 A.M.

Ⓑ 10:15 A.M.

Ⓒ 10:30 A.M.

Ⓓ 10:45 A.M.

23. Sandy cut three pieces of yarn to use for her art project. One piece was 1 foot 8 inches long, one was 10 inches long, and one was 2 feet 6 inches long. How much yarn did Sandy use?

Ⓐ 3 feet 12 inches

Ⓑ 4 feet 10 inches

Ⓒ 5 feet

Ⓓ 5 feet 6 inches

24. A picture called a mosaic was made from 172,435 small clay tiles. What is the value of the digit 2 in 172,435?

Ⓐ 200

Ⓑ 2,000

Ⓒ 20,000

Ⓓ 200,000

25. Maya used number tiles to make the number 428,745. Then she changed two digits to make the number 427,845. Which statement about these numbers is correct?

Ⓐ 428,745 < 427,845

Ⓑ 427,845 = 428,745

Ⓒ 427,845 > 428,745

Ⓓ 427,845 < 428,745

GO ON ➡

26. An amusement park had 56,437 visitors the first year and 48,319 visitors the second year it was open. What was the total number of visitors for both years?

(A) 114,756 visitors

(B) 104,756 visitors

(C) 104,746 visitors

(D) 94,746 visitors

27. Mika and Shelly were playing a video game. Mika scored 65,324 points. Shelly scored 46,789 points. How many more points did Mika score than Shelly?

(A) 28,645

(B) 28,535

(C) 18,645

(D) 18,535

28. The lunch room at Diane's school has a perimeter of 300 feet. The length of the room is 85 feet. What is the width of the room?

(A) 50 feet

(B) 65 feet

(C) 75 feet

(D) 150 feet

29. Patel made a rectangular garden in his family's backyard

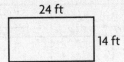

24 ft

14 ft

What is the perimeter of the garden?

(A) 336 feet

(B) 76 feet

(C) 48 feet

(D) 38 feet

30. Patrick drew this plan for a new walkway through his backyard

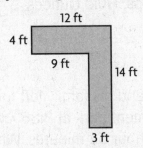

12 ft

4 ft

9 ft

14 ft

3 ft

How many square feet of bricks will Patrick need to cover the walkway?

(A) 168 square feet

(B) 90 square feet

(C) 78 square feet

(D) 52 square feet

GO ON ➡

31. Philip is making a poster that is 36 inches long and 24 inches wide. He cuts out a rectangle that is 5 inches long and 12 inches wide from the poster. How much of the poster remains?

   (A) 140 square inches

   (B) 704 square inches

   (C) 804 square inches

   (D) 864 square inches

32. Which shows the **best** estimate to use to find 43×78?

   (A) $40 \times 70 = 2,800$

   (B) $40 \times 80 = 3,200$

   (C) $50 \times 70 = 3,500$

   (D) $50 \times 80 = 4,000$

33. Chen can jump rope 60 times a minute. At that rate, how many jumps can he make in 9 minutes?

   (A) 620

   (B) 540

   (C) 520

   (D) 500

34. Marjorie's customers bought 94 bouquets at her flower shop for $14 each. What is the total amount customers paid for the bouquets?

   (A) $1,216

   (B) $1,306

   (C) $1,316

   (D) $1,416

35. Use comparative relational thinking to find the unknown number.

$$116 + 58 = 135 + n$$

   (A) $n = 31$

   (B) $n = 33$

   (C) $n = 39$

   (D) $n = 174$

GO ON

36. Matt is making a picture frame from a piece of wood trim that is $\frac{27}{8}$ feet long. How can Matt rename the fraction as a mixed number?

Ⓐ $3\frac{3}{8}$

Ⓑ $2\frac{3}{8}$

Ⓒ $2\frac{1}{4}$

Ⓓ $1\frac{3}{8}$

37. Suki named a fraction that was **not** a multiple of $\frac{3}{4}$. Which fraction could she have named?

Ⓐ $\frac{6}{4}$

Ⓑ $\frac{9}{4}$

Ⓒ $\frac{10}{4}$

Ⓓ $\frac{12}{4}$

38. Larry rides his bike $\frac{5}{6}$ mile 4 times a week. How far does Larry ride his bike each week?

Ⓐ $3\frac{1}{3}$ miles

Ⓑ $3\frac{2}{3}$ miles

Ⓒ 4 miles

Ⓓ 20 miles

39. Jason's soccer practice lasts for $1\frac{1}{3}$ hours. He goes to practice 4 days a week. How much time in all does Jason spend at soccer practice?

Ⓐ $6\frac{2}{3}$ hours

Ⓑ $6\frac{1}{3}$ hours

Ⓒ $5\frac{2}{3}$ hours

Ⓓ $5\frac{1}{3}$ hours

40. At the beginning of the school year, 118 students are enrolled in 4th grade. The students are divided into 6 classes. Which is the **best** estimate of the number of students in each class?

Ⓐ 10

Ⓑ 20

Ⓒ 30

Ⓓ 40

GO ON

Name _____

41. The art teacher needs 70 markers for her classes. The markers come in packages of 15. What is the smallest number of packages of markers the art teacher will need to buy?

Ⓐ 5

Ⓑ 4

Ⓒ 3

Ⓓ 2

44. Brad drew the figure below.

How many lines of symmetry does the figure have?

Ⓐ 4

Ⓑ 3

Ⓒ 2

Ⓓ 1

42. A movie theater sold 2,604 tickets in 6 days. They sold the same number of tickets each day. How many tickets did the theater sell each day?

Ⓐ 404

Ⓑ 434

Ⓒ 443

Ⓓ 534

45. Connie drew the figure below as an example for her classmate.

•———————•

Which of the following terms **best** describes the figure Connie drew?

Ⓐ line segment

Ⓑ line

Ⓒ angle

Ⓓ ray

43. A pencil company packs pencils in boxes of 8. How many boxes can they pack with 32,000 pencils?

Ⓐ 40,000

Ⓑ 4,000

Ⓒ 400

Ⓓ 40

GO ON ➡

46. A window is in the shape of a trapezoid. Which figure could be the shape of the window?

Ⓐ

Ⓑ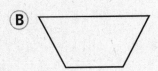

Ⓒ

Ⓓ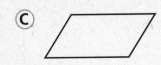

47. A flag is in the shape of a right triangle. Which of the following could be the shape of the flag?

Ⓐ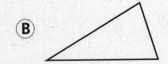

Ⓑ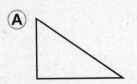

Ⓒ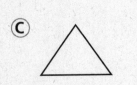

Ⓓ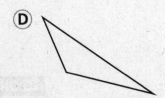

48. Andy walked $\frac{3}{4}$ of a mile to the post office and another $\frac{1}{2}$ mile to the supermarket. Which number is a common denominator for $\frac{3}{4}$ and $\frac{1}{2}$?

Ⓐ 10

Ⓑ 8

Ⓒ 6

Ⓓ 5

49. Simon bought $\frac{6}{8}$ of a pound of tuna salad for sandwiches. Which fraction is equivalent to $\frac{6}{8}$?

Ⓐ $\frac{2}{4}$

Ⓑ $\frac{1}{2}$

Ⓒ $\frac{2}{3}$

Ⓓ $\frac{12}{16}$

50. Anita mixes $\frac{3}{5}$ pound of peanuts with $\frac{3}{8}$ pound of raisins to make a snack. Which statement correctly compares the fractions?

Ⓐ $\frac{3}{8} = \frac{3}{5}$

Ⓑ $\frac{3}{8} > \frac{3}{5}$

Ⓒ $\frac{3}{5} > \frac{3}{8}$

Ⓓ $\frac{3}{5} < \frac{3}{8}$

STOP

1. Explain how to find 30×80 using mental math.

```


```

2. Mr. Burn's class is taking a field trip to the planetarium. The trip will cost $27 for each student. There are 18 students in his class.

Part A

Round each factor to estimate the total cost of the field trip.

```


```

Part B

Use compatible numbers to estimate the total cost of the field trip.

```


```

Part C

Which do you think is the better estimate? Explain.

```


```

GO ON

3. For numbers 3a–3e, select Yes or No to show if the answer is correct.

3a. $75 \times 10 = 750$ ○ Yes   ○ No

3b. $14 \times 20 = 280$ ○ Yes   ○ No

3c. $60 \times 30 = 180$ ○ Yes   ○ No

3d. $50 \times 50 = 2,500$ ○ Yes   ○ No

3e. $14 \times 30 = 700$ ○ Yes   ○ No

4. There are 28 boxes of pens in Mr. Gardner's supply cabinet. Each box contains 100 pens. How many pens are in the supply cabinet?

_____ pens

5. Which would provide a reasonable estimate for each product? Write the estimate beside the product. An estimate may be used more than once.

50×20	25×40	30×30

26×37 [ ] 28×31 [ ]

51×21 [ ] 41×24 [ ]

6. There are 23 classes in the fourth grade. Each grade has 21 students. Write a number sentence that will provide a reasonable estimate for the number of students in the fourth grade. Explain how you found your estimate.

GO ON

7. The model shows 41 × 32. Write the partial products.

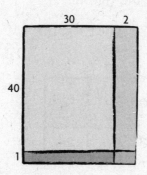

8. Albert made this model to find the product 28 × 43. His model is incorrect.

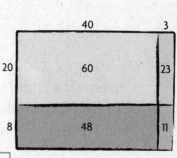

$43 \times 28 = 142$

Part A

What did Albert do wrong?

Part B

Redraw the model so that it is correct.

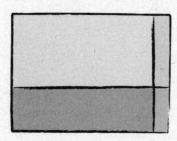

Part C

What is the product 28 × 43?

9. Tatum wants to use partial products to find 12 × 36. Write the numbers in the boxes to show 12 × 36.

(□ × □) + (□ × □) + (□ × □) + (□ × □)

GO ON

10. Which model can be used to find the product? Write the letter of the multiplication problem below the model.

Ⓐ 17 × 35   Ⓑ 26 × 14   Ⓒ 13 × 33

	30	3
10	300	30
3	90	9

	30	5
10	300	50
7	210	35

	10	4
20	200	80
6	60	24

_____   _____   _____

11. Mr. Thomas places orders for pencils with the school emblem. The order includes 15 boxes of pencils and each box holds 25 pencils. How many pencils does Mr. Thomas order? Use partial products to help you find the answer.

12. Write the unknown digits. Use each digit exactly once.

```
      51
  ×   28
  ─────────
  1, □ 00
    □ 00
     □ 0
  + □
  ─────────
  □ ,428
```

| 1 | 2 | 4 | 8 | 0 |

13. Alex has 21 marbles. Zach has 19 times as many marbles as Alex. How many marbles does Zach have?

_____ marbles

14. Multiply.

51 × 13 = _____

GO ON

15. A farmer planted 38 rows of green beans with 17 plants in each row. How many green bean plants did the farmer grow?

_____ green bean plants

16. Select another way to show 23 × 29. Mark all that apply.

Ⓐ (23 × 20) + (23 × 9)

Ⓑ (23 × 20) + (23 × 2) + (23 × 20) + (23 × 9)

Ⓒ (20 × 29) + (3 × 20) + (3 × 9)

Ⓓ (23 × 20) + (23 × 3)

Ⓔ (20 × 20) + (20 × 9) + (3 × 20) + (3 × 9)

17. Val runs 13 laps. Each lap is 72 meters. How many meters does Van run? Show your work.

18. The school principal orders 6 new chalkboards for each grade. There are 3 grades in the school. Each new chalkboard cost $98. What is the total cost for the new chalkboards? Explain how you found your answer.

19. Bill and Alyssa helped pack books to donate to a charity. Bill packed 28 boxes with 30 books in each box. Alyssa packed 31 boxes with 25 books in each box. How many more books did Bill pack? Show your work.

GO ON ➡

20. Steve and Bradley are finding the product of 25 and 21.

Steve	Bradley
25	25
× 21	× 21
250	400
+ 500	10
750	20
	+ 5
	435

Part A

Steve's answer is incorrect. What did Steve do wrong?

Part B

Bradley's answer is also incorrect. What did Bradley do wrong?

Part C

What is the correct product?

21. A music store sells 22 blue MP3 players and 27 red MP3 players. Each MP3 player costs $41.

Part A

What is a reasonable estimate for the total cost of the MP3 players? Show or explain how you found your answer.

Part B

What is the exact answer for the total cost of the MP3 players? Show or explain how you found your answer.

1. Kelli and her family went to the beach for vacation. They drove 293 miles in 7 hours to get there. If they drove the same number of miles each hour, about how many miles did they drive each hour? Select the numbers the quotient is between.

   (A) 40   (B) 50   (C) 60   (D) 70   (E) 80

2. Between which two numbers is the quotient of 88 ÷ 5? Write the numbers in the boxes.

   5   10   15   20   25

   The quotient is between ☐ and ☐.

3. Look at the model. What division does it show?

   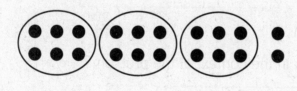

   _____ ÷ _____ ⟶ _____ r _____

4. For 4a–4d, choose Yes or No to tell whether the division sentence has a remainder.

   4a. 32 ÷ 4   ○ Yes   ○ No

   4b. 41 ÷ 3   ○ Yes   ○ No

   4c. 65 ÷ 4   ○ Yes   ○ No

   4d. 36 ÷ 9   ○ Yes   ○ No

GO ON

5. The harbormaster decides how many trips the ferry needs to make for 37 cars. The ferry can carry 8 cars at a time. What is the best way to interpret the remainder of 37 ÷ 8 so that all cars can cross the harbor?

_____

6. Kira makes 93 greeting cards for a craft fair. She sells the cards in packs of 5. How many full packs of greeting cards does Kira make?

_____ packs

7. A kennel is moving 160 dogs to a new facility. Each dog has its own crate. The facility manager rents 17 trucks. Each truck holds 9 dogs in their crates.

Part A

Write a division problem that can be used to find the number of trucks needed to carry the dogs in their crates. Then solve.

_____

Part B

What does the remainder mean in the context of the problem?

_____

Part C

How can you use your answer to determine if the facility manager rented enough trucks? Explain.

_____

8. Solve.

4,500 ÷ 9 = _____

GO ON

9. Which quotients are equal to 600? Mark all that apply.

Ⓐ 1,200 ÷ 2   Ⓒ 2,400 ÷ 4   Ⓔ 420 ÷ 7

Ⓑ 180 ÷ 3   Ⓓ 3,000 ÷ 5   Ⓕ 6,000 ÷ 3

10. Liz estimated 228 ÷ 7 to be between 30 and 40. Which basic facts did she use to help her estimate? Mark all that apply.

Ⓐ 20 ÷ 5   Ⓑ 21 ÷ 7   Ⓒ 28 ÷ 7   Ⓓ 30 ÷ 5

11. Amanda and her four sisters divided 1,021 stickers equally. About how many stickers did each girl receive?

12. For numbers 12a–12d, choose Yes or No to show how to use the Distributive Property to break apart the dividend to find the quotient 128 ÷ 4.

12a. (100 ÷ 4) + (28 ÷ 4)   ○ Yes   ○ No

12b. (103 ÷ 4) + (25 ÷ 4)   ○ Yes   ○ No

12c. (64 ÷ 4) + (64 ÷ 4)   ○ Yes   ○ No

12d. (12 ÷ 4) + (28 ÷ 4)   ○ Yes   ○ No

13. There are 48 people waiting for a fishing tour. Each boat holds 12 people. Rodney used the work below to find the number of boats needed. Explain how Rodney's work can be used to find the number of boats needed.

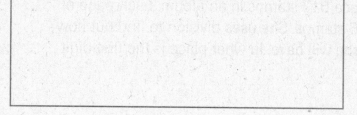

```
12)48
  -12
   36
  -12
   24
  -12
   12
  -12
    0
```

GO ON

14. A science show brings along everything it needs for a show in big trucks.

Part A

The science show sets up chairs in rows with 8 seats in each row. How many rows will need to be set up if 456 people are expected to attend the show?

_____ rows

Part B

Can the rows be divided into a number of equal sections? Explain how you found your answer.

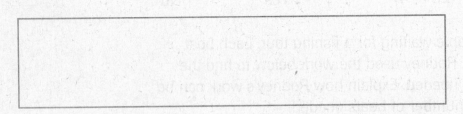

Part C

The lizards in the show eat about 250 crickets per week. About how many crickets do the lizards eat each day? Explain.

15. Sylvia plans to place 617 stamps in an album. Each page of the album holds 5 stamps. She uses division to find out how many full pages she will have. In what place is the first digit of the quotient?

_____

16. Which model matches each expression? Write the letter in the box next to the model.

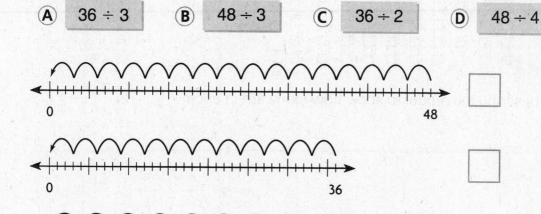

Ⓐ 36 ÷ 3   Ⓑ 48 ÷ 3   Ⓒ 36 ÷ 2   Ⓓ 48 ÷ 4

17. Diego bought 488 frozen yogurt bars in 4 different flavors for a party. He bought the same number of each flavor. How many of each flavor did he buy?

_____ bars of each flavor

18. Use partial quotients. Fill in the blanks.

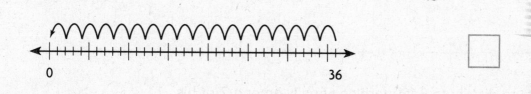

7)749

−[ ]   100 × 7   [ ]
___
[ ]
−[ ]   7 × 7   + [ ]
___   ___
[ ]   [ ]

GO ON

19. Ethan needs to divide these base-ten blocks into 3 equal groups.

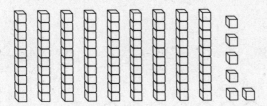

Draw or describe the model to show how many are in each group.

20. Jake wants to distribute 543 marbles equally among 7 of his friends. In which place is the first digit of the quotient? Choose the word that makes the sentence true.

The first digit of the quotient is in the

| ones |
| tens |
| hundreds |
| thousands |

place.

21. Chad bought 8 dozen note pads for his office. The note pads were divided equally into 6 boxes. How many note pads are in each box?

_____ note pads

22. There are 126 seats in a meeting room. There are 9 seats in each row. There are 90 people seated, filling up full rows of seats. How many rows are empty?

_____ rows

1. List all of the factors of the number.

21: _____

2. Select the numbers that have a factor of 6. Mark all that apply.

- (A) 12
- (B) 3
- (C) 42
- (D) 6
- (E) 48
- (F) 31

3. Marissa was decorating her room. She arranged 63 picture tiles on a wall in the shape of a rectangle. For 3a–3e, choose Yes or No to tell whether a possible arrangement of the picture tiles is shown.

3a. 7 rows of 9 tiles   ○ Yes   ○ No

3b. 22 rows of 6 tiles   ○ Yes   ○ No

3c. 21 rows of 3 tiles   ○ Yes   ○ No

3d. 63 rows of 1 tile   ○ Yes   ○ No

3e. 32 rows of 2 tiles   ○ Yes   ○ No

4. List all the factor pairs in the table.

Factors of 54	
____ × ____ = ____	____ , ____
____ × ____ = ____	____ , ____
____ × ____ = ____	____ , ____
____ × ____ = ____	____ , ____

GO ON

5. Classify the numbers. Some numbers may belong in more than one box.

45　48　81　84　99

Divisible by 3 and 9	Divisible by 5 and 9	Divisible by 2 and 6

6. Josh works in a balloon store. He will put 45 balloons into bunches. He must use the same number of balloons in each bunch. The number of balloons in each bunch must be greater than 1 and less than 10. How many balloons could be in each bunch?

_____ balloons

7. Miles has a train collection with 36 engines, 72 boxcars, and 18 cabooses. He wants to arrange the train cars in equal rows with only one type of train car in each row. How many can he put in each row? Mark all that apply.

Ⓐ 12　　Ⓑ 6　　Ⓒ 4　　Ⓓ 3　　Ⓔ 2　　Ⓕ 1

8. The library is designing a book display with 20 fiction books, 28 biographies, and 40 non-fiction books. Each shelf will have only one type of book on it. Sheena says she can put 5 books on each shelf. She listed the common factors of 20, 28, and 40 below to support her reasoning.

20: 1, 2, 3, 4, 5, 7, 20

28: 1, 2, 4, 5, 14, 28

40: 1, 2, 4, 5, 8, 10, 20, 40

Is she correct? Explain your answer. If her reasoning is incorrect, explain how she should have found the answer.

GO ON

9. The number of books featured at the local library is shown in the table.

Books	
Type of Book	**Number of Books**
mystery	32
novel	16
non-fiction	12

Part A

The local library is hosting a book fair in August that features the mystery books. All authors discuss the same number of mystery books and each will discuss more than 1 mystery book. How many authors could be featured in the show?

_____

Part B

The library wants to display all the books on shelves in rows. Each row has the same number of books and the same type of books. How many books could be in each row? Explain how you found your answer.

10. Beverly was skip counting while jumping rope. She started to count by 9s. She said 9, 18, 27, 36, 45, and 54. What number will she say next?

_____

11. Jose wrote the number 36. If his rule is *add 6*, what is the fourth number in Jose's pattern? How can you check your answer?

12. For numbers 12a–12e, select True or False for each
statement.

12a. The number 45 is a
multiple of 9.   ○ True   ○ False

12b. The number 6 is a
multiple of 12.   ○ True   ○ False

12c. The number 56 is a
multiple of 8.   ○ True   ○ False

12d. The number 4 is a
factor of 8.   ○ True   ○ False

12e. The number 36 is a
factor of 9.   ○ True   ○ False

13. What multiple of 9 is also a factor of 9?

14. Marta uses 1 piece of paper and 1 piece of ribbon to make
kites. The paper comes in packs of 3 pieces and the ribbon
comes in packs of 4 pieces. What is the least number of kites
Marta can make without any supplies left over?

_____ kites

15. A store in Roger's neighborhood sells boxes of pencils that
have 6 pencils in each box. Roger bought several boxes of
pencils at the store. Which could be the number of pencils
he bought? Mark all that apply.

(A) 9   (B) 18   (C) 20   (D) 24   (E) 34   (F) 42

16. Choose the words that make the sentence true.

The number 12 is | prime / composite | because it has | exactly / more than | two factors.

GO ON ▶

17. Gus wrote the following riddle: I am a number between 30 and 60.
My ones digit is three less than my tens digit. I am a prime number.

Part A

What number does Gus' riddle describe? Explain.

Part B

Gus' friend Russ guessed that his riddle was about the number 47.
Why can't 47 be the answer to Gus' riddle? Explain.

18. Classify the numbers as prime or composite.

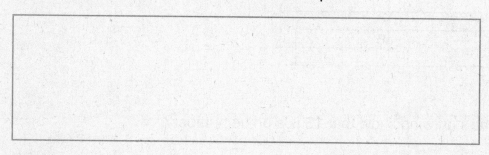

Prime	Composite

19. Aidan makes 12 bracelets on Monday. He makes 8 more bracelets
each day from Tuesday through Thursday. How many bracelets
does Aidan make on Friday?

_____ bracelets

20. Use the rule to write the first five terms of the pattern.

Rule: Add 8, subtract 4   First term: 13

GO ON

21. Eric had 13 tiles to arrange in a rectangular design for the top of a box. He drew a model of the rectangles he could make with the 13 tiles.

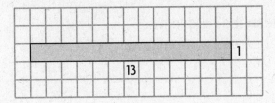

Part A

How does Eric's drawing show that 13 is a prime number?

Part B

Suppose Eric used 12 tiles to make the rectangular design. How many different rectangles could he make with the 12 tiles? Write a list or draw a picture to show the number and dimensions of the rectangles he could make.

Part C

Eric's friend Dawn said that she could make a larger number of different designs with 15 tiles than with Eric's 13 tiles. Do you agree with Dawn? Explain.

1. For numbers 1a–1d, tell whether the fractions are equivalent by selecting the correct symbol.

1a. $\frac{3}{8}$ | $=$ / $\neq$ | $\frac{12}{24}$

1c. $\frac{6}{20}$ | $=$ / $\neq$ | $\frac{3}{10}$

1b. $\frac{6}{7}$ | $=$ / $\neq$ | $\frac{18}{21}$

1d. $\frac{12}{16}$ | $=$ / $\neq$ | $\frac{3}{5}$

2. The table shows the distances of some places in town from the school.

Distance from School	
Place	**Distance**
Library	$\frac{3}{5}$ mile
Post Office	$\frac{1}{2}$ mile
Park	$\frac{3}{4}$ mile
Town Hall	$\frac{8}{10}$ mile

From least to greatest, order the locations by their distance from school.

3. Nicolette needs $\frac{1}{3}$ yard of fabric for her quilt. Write $\frac{1}{3}$ as an equivalent fraction with the denominators shown.

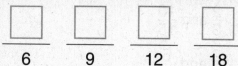

□ / 6   □ / 9   □ / 12   □ / 18

4. Juan has wrenches with the sizes shown below. Write each fraction in the correct box.

$\frac{1}{8}$ in. $\frac{5}{8}$ in. $\frac{8}{16}$ in. $\frac{9}{16}$ in. $\frac{15}{16}$ in. $\frac{5}{16}$ in.

less than $\frac{1}{2}$ in.	equal to $\frac{1}{2}$ in.	greater than $\frac{1}{2}$ in.

GO ON

5. Cassie bought $\frac{3}{8}$ pound of peanuts and $\frac{1}{4}$ pound of cashews to make mixed nuts. Use the numbers to compare the amounts of peanuts and cashews Cassie bought.

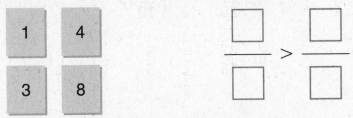

6. Elise is doing her homework. She spends $\frac{1}{3}$ hour on math homework and $\frac{1}{5}$ hour on spelling words. For numbers 6a–6c, select Yes or No to tell whether each of the following is a true statement.

6a.   15 is a common denominator of $\frac{1}{3}$ and $\frac{1}{5}$.   ○ Yes   ○ No

6b.   The amount of time spent on math homework
      can be rewritten as $\frac{1}{15}$.   ○ Yes   ○ No

6c.   The amount of time spent on spelling words can
      be rewritten as $\frac{3}{15}$.   ○ Yes   ○ No

7. In the school band, $\frac{6}{24}$ of the members play the trumpet. In simplest form, what fraction of the band plays the trumpet?

_____ of the band

8. Which pairs of fractions are equivalent? Mark all that apply.

   ○ $\frac{4}{5}$ and $\frac{8}{12}$ ○ $\frac{2}{3}$ and $\frac{10}{15}$

   ○ $\frac{1}{6}$ and $\frac{3}{18}$ ○ $\frac{2}{7}$ and $\frac{6}{20}$

9. Allie worked for $\frac{1}{2}$ hour on Saturday and $\frac{2}{3}$ hour on Sunday. What are four common denominators for the fractions? Explain your reasoning.

GO ON

10. Liam works in a toy store that sells bags of marbles. He puts 10 marbles in each bag, and $\frac{4}{10}$ of the marbles are striped.

Part A

If Liam makes 3 bags of marbles, how many striped marbles does he need? Show how you can check your answer.

_____ striped marbles

Part B

Yesterday Liam used 20 striped marbles to fill bags. How many non-striped marbles did he use to fill the bags? Explain your reasoning.

_____ non-striped marbles

11. In Jason's homeroom, $\frac{8}{30}$ of the students like soccer best, $\frac{6}{15}$ like volleyball best, and $\frac{5}{15}$ like baseball best. For numbers 11a–11c, select True or False for each statement.

11a. In simplest form, $\frac{2}{15}$ of the students like soccer best.　　○ True　　○ False

11b. In simplest form, $\frac{3}{5}$ of the students like volleyball best.　　○ True　　○ False

11c. In simplest form, $\frac{1}{3}$ of the students like baseball best.　　○ True　　○ False

GO ON ➡

12. Edgar, Jack, and Katie walked around Woodbury Lake. Edgar walked $\frac{3}{5}$ of the distance in an hour. Jack walked $\frac{3}{4}$ of the distance in an hour. Ellen walked $\frac{6}{8}$ of the distance in an hour. Compare the distances walked by each person by matching the statements to the correct symbol. Each symbol may be used more than once or not at all.

$\frac{3}{5} \bigcirc \frac{3}{4}$ •   • <

$\frac{6}{8} \bigcirc \frac{3}{4}$ •   • >

$\frac{3}{5} \bigcirc \frac{6}{8}$ •   • =

13. Olivia is using her grandmother's chili recipe. Some of the ingredients for the recipe are given.

Chili Recipe	
$\frac{1}{2}$ cup chopped onion	$\frac{1}{4}$ cup diced green pepper
$\frac{7}{8}$ cup tomato sauce	$\frac{3}{4}$ cup tomato soup
$\frac{5}{6}$ cup tomato puree	$\frac{3}{6}$ cup salsa

Part A

Which ingredient does Olivia use the greater amount of, tomato sauce or tomato soup? Explain how you found your answer.

Part B

Olivia says that she needs the same amount of two different ingredients. Is she correct? Support your answer with information from the problem.

GO ON

14. Craig is tiling the floor of his bathroom. He wants $\frac{1}{4}$ of the tiles to be brown. What other fractions can represent the part of the tiles that will be brown? Shade the models to show your work.

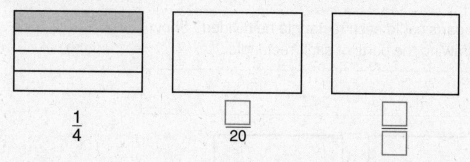

$\frac{1}{4}$ $\frac{\Box}{20}$ $\frac{\Box}{\Box}$

15. Georgina has $\frac{3}{8}$ yard of blue fabric and $\frac{1}{4}$ yard of red fabric. Does she have the same amount of blue and red fabric?
Shade the model to show how you found your answer.
Explain your reasoning.

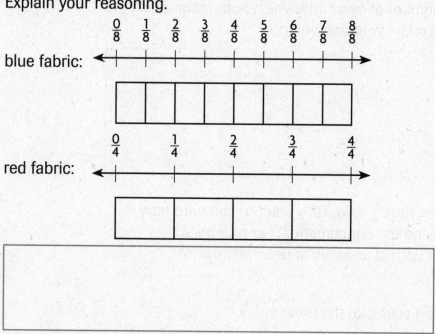

16. Martin fills an aquarium $\frac{4}{5}$ full of water. Fill in each box with a number from the list to generate equivalent fractions for $\frac{4}{5}$. Not all numbers will be used.

5	6	8	10
12	15	20	25

$$\frac{4}{5} = \frac{\Box}{10} = \frac{12}{\Box} = \frac{\Box}{\Box}$$

GO ON ➡

17. Henry has two same-size rectangles divided into the same number of equal parts. One rectangle has $\frac{2}{5}$ of the parts shaded, and the other has $\frac{1}{2}$ of the parts shaded.

Part A

Into how many parts could each rectangle be divided? Show your work by drawing the parts of each rectangle.

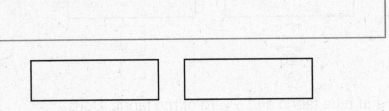

Part B

Is there more than one possible answer to Part A? If so, did you find the least number of parts into which both rectangles could be divided? Explain your reasoning.

18. Ann runs $\frac{2}{5}$ mile. Kim runs $\frac{3}{4}$ mile. They want to compare how far they each ran using the benchmark $\frac{1}{2}$. For numbers 18a–18c, select the correct answers to describe how to solve the problem.

18a. Compare Ann's distance to the benchmark: $\frac{2}{5}$
$$\begin{array}{c} < \\ > \\ = \end{array}$$
$\frac{1}{2}$.

18b. Compare Kim's distance to the benchmark: $\frac{3}{4}$
$$\begin{array}{c} < \\ > \\ = \end{array}$$
$\frac{1}{2}$.

18c. Ann ran
| farther than |
| the same distance as |
| less than |
 Kim.

1. For numbers 1a–1e, select Yes or No to indicate if a rectangle with the given dimensions would have a perimeter of 60 inches.

   1a. length: 15 inches   width: 15 inches   ○ Yes   ○ No

   1b. length: 20 inches   width: 10 inches   ○ Yes   ○ No

   1c. length: 25 inches   width: 4 inches   ○ Yes   ○ No

   1d. length: 27 inches   width: 3 inches   ○ Yes   ○ No

   1e. length: 30 inches   width: 2 inches   ○ Yes   ○ No

2. Diane made a design using a small square, a medium square, and a large square. She shaded the small square and the outer region.

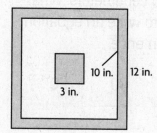

Part A

What is the area of each of the 3 squares she drew? Show your work.

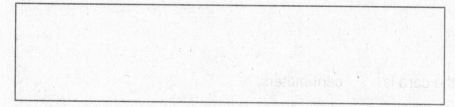

Part B

What is the area that is shaded? Explain how you found your answer.

GO ON

3. Match the dimensions of the rectangles in the top row with the correct area or perimeter in the bottom row.

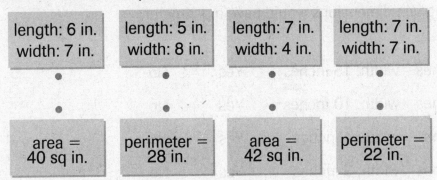

length: 6 in.
width: 7 in.

length: 5 in.
width: 8 in.

length: 7 in.
width: 4 in.

length: 7 in.
width: 7 in.

area =
40 sq in.

perimeter =
28 in.

area =
42 sq in.

perimeter =
22 in.

4. Karlie painted a portrait. The height of the portrait measures 14 inches. The width is half as long as the height. What is the area of the portrait?

_____ square inches

5. Wilma used 60 centimeters of lace to make a border around a rectangular card. The width of the card is 20 centimeters. What is the length of the card? Use the numbers to write an equation and solve. A number may be used more than once.

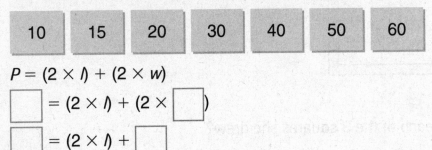

| 10 | 15 | 20 | 30 | 40 | 50 | 60 |

$P = (2 \times l) + (2 \times w)$

$\boxed{} = (2 \times l) + (2 \times \boxed{})$

$\boxed{} = (2 \times l) + \boxed{}$

$\boxed{} = 2 \times l$

$\boxed{} = l$

So, the length of the card is $\boxed{}$ centimeters.

6. Bill drew a rectangle with a perimeter of 16 inches. Then he tried to draw a square with a perimeter of 16 inches.

Draw 3 different rectangles that Bill could have drawn. Then draw the square, if possible.

GO ON ▶

Name _____

7. Gretchen and Ed are drawing plans for rectangular play areas. In Gretchen's plan, the play area is 15 feet by 12 feet. In Ed's plan the play area is 14 feet by 14 feet. For numbers 7a–7d, select True or False for each statement.

7a. The area of Ed's play area is 56 square feet.　　○ True　　○ False

7b. The area of Gretchen's play area is 180 square feet.　　○ True　　○ False

7c. Gretchen's play area has a greater area than Ed's play area.　　○ True　　○ False

7d. The area of Ed's play area is 16 square feet greater than Gretchen's.　　○ True　　○ False

8. Laura bought a square canvas to paint a picture of her cat. One side measures 22 centimeters. What is the area of the canvas? Show your work.

9. Adrian bought a frame for a photograph that he took.

```
          24 in.
     Frame
        20 in.


            8 in.   10 in.
```

What is the area of the frame not covered by the picture?

_____ square inches

10. A farmer has 200 feet of fencing to use for a chicken pen. He wants the width of the pen to be 27 feet. Draw a rectangle that could be the space for the chicken pen. Label the length and the width.

GO ON

11. The diagram shows the dimensions of Anna's laundry
room floor.

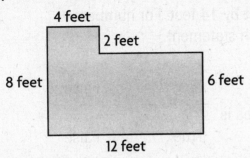

Use either addition or subtraction to find the area of the floor
of the laundry room. Show your work.

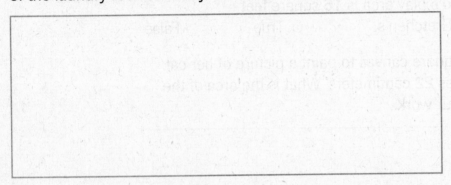

12. One wall of Patel's bedroom is 13 feet wide and 8 feet tall.
A window on the wall is 3 feet high and 6 feet long. Which
statement tells how to find the amount of wallpaper Patel
would need to cover this wall? Mark all that apply.

Ⓐ Add 13 + 8 + 3 + 6.

Ⓑ Add 13 × 8 and 3 × 6.

Ⓒ Subtract 18 from 13 × 8.

Ⓓ Subtract 8 × 6 from 13 × 3.

Ⓔ Subtract 13 × 8 from 3 × 6.

Ⓕ Subtract 3 × 6 from 13 × 8.

13. A row of lockers covers 160 square feet of space along a
wall. If the lockers are 5 feet tall, what length along the wall
do they cover?

_____ feet

GO ON ➡

14. Mr. Benson built a play area for his children and an office for himself.

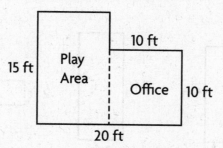

Explain how he can find the amount of carpet he needs to cover the floor in both rooms. Then find the amount of carpet he will need.

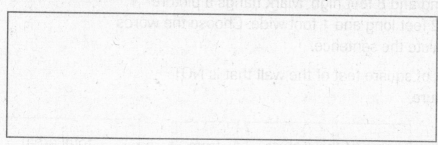

15. Workers are fencing off a rectangular construction zone before they begin work. The length of the construction zone is 20 meters. The width of the construction zone is 5 meters less than the length.

How much fence do the workers need to enclose the construction zone? Explain how you found your answer.

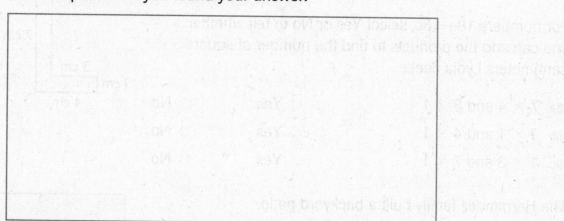

GO ON

16. Which rectangle has a perimeter of 20 feet? Mark all that apply.

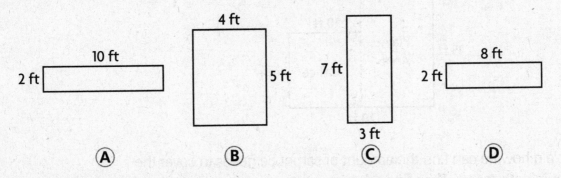

4 ft

10 ft

2 ft

5 ft

7 ft

3 ft

8 ft

2 ft

Ⓐ   Ⓑ   Ⓒ   Ⓓ

17. A wall is 12 feet long and 8 feet high. Mark hangs a picture on the wall that is 2 feet long and 1 foot wide. Choose the words that correctly complete the sentence.

To find the number of square feet of the wall that is NOT covered by the picture,

multiply		area of the picture	from		total area.
add	the	width of the wall	by	the	area of the wall.
subtract		area of the wall	to		area of the picture.

18. Lydia is cutting the shape from a piece of construction paper.

For numbers 18a–18c, select Yes or No to tell whether you can add the products to find the number of square centimeters Lydia needs.

7 cm

3 cm

1 cm

4 cm

18a. 7×4 and 3×1 ○ Yes   ○ No

18b. 7×1 and 4×1 ○ Yes   ○ No

18c. 1×3 and 7×1 ○ Yes   ○ No

19. The Hernandez family built a backyard patio.

The width and length of the patio are whole numbers. What could be the dimensions of the patio?

Area = 150 square feet

STOP

An Amusement Park

Each year, the Park Director at an amusement park records the number of tickets sold for the five rides at her park.

Name of Ride	Tickets Sold
Wild Mouse	314,890
Tilt-a-Whirl	198,572
Big Roller Coaster	255,429
Water Slide	320,040
Spinning Tea Cups	189,403

1. Find the value of the ten thousands place for the Big Roller Coaster. How is the value of the digit in the ten thousands place different from the value of the digit in the thousands place?

   _____

   _____

2. For which ride does the number of tickets sold have an 8 in the greatest place value? Explain how you know.

   _____

   _____

3. Compare the number of tickets sold for the Wild Mouse and the Water Slide. Write a number sentence using >, <, or =. Explain your answer.

   _____

   _____

4. Choose one ride in the chart. Write the number of tickets sold in the box below. Then write the number in expanded form and in word form.

```
┌─────────────────┐
│                 │
│                 │
│                 │
└─────────────────┘
```

_____

_____

5. The Park Director also records the number of visitors each week. For each number of visitors, round to the place value of **the underlined digit.**

Week	Number of Visitors	Rounded Number
1	12<u>7</u>,862	
2	110,3<u>5</u>1	
3	<u>9</u>4,678	

6. Use the numbers in the chart to solve the problems. Estimate. Show your work.

a. About how many people visited the amusement park during Week 2 and Week 3?

Estimate: _____

b. About how many more people visited the amusement park during Week 1 than Week 3?

Estimate: _____

Cars, Trains, Boats, and Planes

Every day people travel to and from a city using various forms of transportation. Use multiplication strategies to solve each problem.

1. To go to the beach, Adiyah drives 4 times as many miles as Jacob. Adiyah drives 20 miles. How many miles does Jacob drive? Write an equation and a comparison sentence to solve.

   _____

   _____

   _____

2. Hannah travels 6 times as many minutes to work as Raoul does. Together, they travel for 63 minutes. How many minutes does Hannah travel? Draw a model and write an equation to solve.

3. Ben travels by train 19 miles to work. If Ben travels 8 times a week, how many miles does he travel? Use a drawing and the Distributive Property to solve. Show your work.

4. A ferryboat travels 178 miles in one week. How many miles does the boat travel in 4 weeks? Draw a diagram and use expanded form to solve. Show your work.

5. The chart shows the distance from New York City to three cities.

Distance from New York City (miles)		
Boston, MA	Rochester, NY	Salt Lake City, UT
217	345	2,171

Estimate your answer. Then find the exact answer. Use rounding, regrouping, or place value. Describe the strategy you used.

a. A plane travels from New York City to Boston once each day. How far does the plane travel in one week on this route?

Estimate _____

Exact answer _____

Strategy _____

b. Another plane makes 6 trips in one week. It travels from New York City to Rochester 3 times, and from New York City to Salt Lake City 3 times. How many miles does the plane travel each week?

Estimate _____

Exact answer _____

Strategy _____

Visiting New York City

A tour group visits New York City. Some of the sights they will visit are shown in the chart below. Use the chart to solve problems 1–3.

Sight	Cost
Bus Tour of Chinatown	$18
Broadway Show	$44
Observation Tower: Main Deck (adult)	$25
Observation Tower: Main Deck (child)	$19
Observation Tower: Top Deck (all visitors)	$32

1. Twenty people on the tour go on the bus tour of Chinatown. How much does it cost in all? Use place value, the Distributive Property, or a number line to solve. Show your work.

2. There are 23 people that go to the Broadway Show. How much does it cost altogether? Draw a simple diagram to model and break apart factors to solve. Show your work.

3. There are 34 adults and 13 children on the tour. How much money
   will the group save by visiting the Main Deck of the Observation Tower
   instead of the Top Deck? Show your work. Explain your answer.

   _____

   _____

4. Postcards come in packages of 16. If 52 tourists each buy one
   package of post cards, how many postcards do they buy in all?

   a. Use partial products to solve. Show your work.

   b. Explain how you can use rounding or compatible numbers to see
      if your answer is reasonable.

   _____

   _____

Helping Hands

Matt, Carlos, and Tavon are helping make repairs to their school building during the summer. Their math teacher, Mr. Johnson, is in charge of the repairs and makes sure the boys get some extra math practice while they help out.

1. A delivery of lumber arrives at the school. Mr. Johnson asks Carlos to show the deliverymen to the classroom that has a number equal to the quotient of $5,286 \div 3$. How many digits will the classroom number have? Explain your mathematical reasoning.

2. Mr. Johnson and the boys are helping paint the school. Mr. Johnson asks Tavon to follow these instructions.

    Divide 2,430 by 9. Then divide that quotient by 6. Take two cans of paint to the classroom that has the same number as the final quotient.

    Choose two different methods to find the answer. Explain your choices and then find the number of the classroom where Tavon should take the cans of paint.

3. Mr. Johnson asked Carlos to take garbage bags to another floor using these instructions.

> Find how many 7s are in 1,762. The remainder is the number of garbage bags you will take. The quotient is the classroom number.

How can Carlos use partial products to find the information he needs? Show and explain your mathematical thinking.

4. Matt had instructions to take a box of nails to a classroom that has a number equal to the remainder of the division $2,960 \div 9$. Matt took the nails to classroom 17. Without performing calculations, tell whether Matt was correct. Explain your mathematical thinking.

Taking the Subway

1. A subway train arrives at the station every 8 minutes. You have a doctor's appointment near the station, so you take the subway and arrive at 10:04. You are finished with your appointment at 11:15. When will the next subway train arrive at the station?

2. Anya's grandfather gives her a collection of souvenir subway tokens. He gives her 9 tokens from the 1960s, 12 tokens from the 1970s, and 21 tokens from the 1980s. She wants to make a display of each type of token. She wants all three displays to have rows with the same number of tokens in them.

   a. How can she display the tokens? Show your work.

   b. Are the number of tokens in each of Anya's collections prime or composite numbers? Explain your reasoning.

   _____

   _____

   _____

3. Nicholas challenges Rajiv with these instructions for finding his house after basketball practice.

> Get on the subway at 14th Street. The subway stops at 23rd, 28th, 33rd, 42nd, 51st, 59th, 68th, 77th, 86th, and 96th Streets. Get off at the first street you come to that is divisible by both 3 and 7.

How can Rajiv solve this problem? At which stop should he get off the subway?

4. A subway inspector has a list of stations he is supposed to inspect that day. The list is shown below.

Thursday Assigned Inspections: B Line						
Station 3	Station 8	Station 6	Station 11	Station 9	Station 14	Station 12

The inspector has torn off the bottom of his schedule by mistake. How can he find out if he is supposed to inspect Station 33 today?

Have a Seat!

1. On one side of a football stadium are 30 suites on the Circle Level. Fourteen of the suites have 24 seats each, and the rest have 18 seats. Tyler says that $\frac{14}{30}$ is the simplest form of the fraction to describe the suites with 24 seats. Is he correct? Use models to support your conclusion and explain why Tyler is correct or incorrect.

_____

_____

_____

_____

2. A downtown auditorium hosts large events. The auditorium can seat 600 people at one time. The sponsors of an awards dinner are using the auditorium for 450 people. The chef has prepared meals for $\frac{3}{4}$ of the usual 600 people. The pastry chef has made enough dessert for $\frac{5}{8}$ of the usual 600 people. The staff has set up $\frac{3}{5}$ of the usual 600 chairs. When the guests arrive, will everybody have a place to sit? Will there be enough meals? Enough dessert? Explain your mathematical thinking.

_____

_____

_____

_____

3. One section of a basketball stadium has 60 seats. During one game, $\frac{5}{12}$ of the fans in this section were fans of the home team and $\frac{11}{30}$ were fans of the visiting team. Without doing any calculations, can you tell whether there were more fans for the home team than the away team? How could you use math to find which team had the most fans in that section?

_____

_____

_____

_____

_____

4. The front portion of the Orchestra section at a music hall includes 20 boxes for people in wheelchairs. For the Thursday night show, $\frac{3}{5}$ of the boxes were occupied. For the Friday night show, $\frac{3}{4}$ of the boxes were occupied. For the Saturday afternoon show, $\frac{7}{10}$ of the boxes were occupied. Using symbols, order the fractions to find which show had the most viewers in wheelchairs. Use models to prove your conclusions.

Lending a Hand

1. Enrique lives with his grandmother in an apartment building for senior citizens. He earns extra money by running errands for some of his grandmother's neighbors. Enrique charges $2 for every $\frac{1}{4}$ hour he spends working. He spent $\frac{2}{4}$ hour going to the deli for Mr. McGuire, $1\frac{1}{4}$ hours delivering papers for the apartment manager, and $\frac{3}{4}$ hour picking up Mrs. Shultz's groceries. Did Enrique earn enough money to buy an $18 DVD? Explain your math reasoning using models.

   _____

   _____

   _____

   _____

2. Enrique's grandmother tried to help him figure out how much he earned this week. This is how she calculated the hours Enrique worked.

$$1\frac{1}{4} + \frac{3}{4} + 2\frac{2}{4} + 1\frac{3}{4} + 1 = 5\frac{9}{16}$$

   Is she correct? If not, explain the error and find the correct sum.

   _____

   _____

   _____

   _____

3. On Saturdays, Enrique charges $2 for every $\frac{1}{6}$ hour he spends running errands. He earned $50 last Saturday. He picked up dry cleaning for Mrs. Abel for $\frac{4}{6}$ hour, ran to the post office for Mr. Kovac for $1\frac{1}{6}$ hours, and swept up the lobby of the building for the apartment manager for $\frac{5}{6}$ hour. He got a $4 tip from Mr. Kovac. How long did it take him to walk Mrs. Camacho's dog and pick up her groceries? Show your work.

4. Enrique charges $5 for every $\frac{1}{5}$ hour he spends walking dogs. In the morning he walks Buttons for $\frac{2}{5}$ hour, Bruno for $\frac{1}{5}$ hour, and Pepper for $\frac{3}{5}$ hour, Monday through Friday. On Saturdays he takes Mimi, Diva, and Coco to the dog park for $\frac{4}{5}$ of an hour. On Wednesday this week it rained and Pepper wanted to stay out for only $\frac{1}{5}$ hour. How many hours did Enrique spend with the dogs this week? Explain your method.

_____

_____

_____

_____

Dollar Days

Mr. Asfour owns a small grocery store. The store is very popular for its fresh fruit and vegetables. On Tuesdays, he offers special deals for $1.00.

Only $1.00	Tuesday DOLLAR DAYS!	Only $1.00
Apples – $\frac{3}{4}$ lb	Oranges – $\frac{1}{4}$ lb	Peaches – $\frac{2}{5}$ lb
Pears – $\frac{3}{8}$ lb	Bananas – $\frac{1}{5}$ lb	Peppers – $\frac{4}{6}$ lb
Limes – $\frac{4}{5}$ lb	Peanuts – $\frac{3}{10}$ lb	Lemons – $\frac{7}{8}$ lb

1. Elaine bought $4 worth of apples and $3 worth of lemons. Did her grocery bag weigh more than or less than $5\frac{1}{4}$ pounds? Use a model to support your answer.

2. Deshi paid $5.00 for two different fruits. His grocery bag weighed between $1\frac{1}{2}$ and $2\frac{1}{2}$ pounds. Which combinations of fruit could he have purchased? Show your work.

_____ $3 worth of pears and $2 worth of apples

_____ $4 worth of pears and $1 worth of apples

_____ $2 worth of pears and $3 worth of apples

3. Mrs. Nazari bought $2\frac{1}{4}$ pounds of apples, $1\frac{3}{5}$ pounds of peaches, and $1\frac{1}{5}$ pounds of bananas. She paid with a $20 bill. How much change did she receive? Show your work.

4. Ming paid $8 for every item except peppers. Was her bag lighter than or heavier than 4 pounds? Show the addition using as few steps as you can.

Taxi!

Taxicabs downtown charge a flat fee of $2.50, plus a state tax of $0.50, plus $0.50 for each $\frac{1}{5}$ mile they travel with a passenger.

1. Explain how you could write $\frac{1}{5}$ mile as a fraction with 10 in the denominator, a fraction with 100 in the denominator, and as a decimal.

    _____

    _____

    _____

    _____

    _____

    _____

2. Travis took a taxicab from his office to a meeting on the other side of town. The cab ride cost $8.50, which includes a $2.00 tip. In decimal form, how far is it from his office to the meeting? Show your work.

3. Mr. and Mrs. Rubin dropped coins when their taxicab hit a pothole. Mrs. Rubin lost 2 quarters, 3 nickels, and 17 pennies. Mr. Rubin lost 6 dimes.

   a. Write the total amount of money Mrs. Rubin lost as a decimal and as a fraction. Show your work.

     _____

   b. Did the Rubins lose more money in quarters or dimes? Compare the decimal amounts using >, <, or =. Explain your answer.

     _____

     _____

   c. What is the total value of the dimes and pennies the Rubins lost? Express your answer as a fraction. Show your work.

     _____

4. Keisha took Mr. Mamood's cab from her apartment building to a dentist appointment across town. She paid $9 for her ride, which included a $2 tip. Mr. Mamood then picked up Neil at the same location and took him to his office. Neil paid $11, which included a $3 tip. What was the total distance Mr. Mamood drove Keisha and Neil? Give your answer as a fraction and as a decimal. Explain your mathematical thinking.

     _____

     _____

     _____

     _____

Quilting Bee

The Art Quilt Gallery has an exhibit of old and new quilts. This is the quilt that Naomi and her mother liked best at the gallery show.

1. Place a check next to each geometric feature found in this quilt pattern. Then label it on the picture of the quilt.

_____ point	_____ quadrilateral
_____ line	_____ parallelogram
_____ line segment	_____ acute triangle
_____ ray	_____ parallel lines
_____ square	_____ rectangle
_____ right triangle	_____ rhombus
_____ right angle	_____ trapezoid
_____ acute angle	_____ obtuse triangle
_____ obtuse angle	_____ perpendicular lines

2. Which shapes in the quilt have line symmetry? Label the figures on the quilt. Then draw the lines of symmetry.

3. Make your own pattern for a quilt. Include a pair of parallel line segments, a pair of perpendicular line segments, two kinds of quadrilaterals, and an obtuse triangle. Include any other shapes you choose. Explain your pattern in words.

_____

_____

_____

Klee Kat

Paul Klee was an artist who painted using geometric shapes. A cat painted by Paul Klee might look something like this.

73°

1. Find these angles in the cat. Use the letters to mark each angle on the drawing as you find it. Then write the angle measures on the drawing. One angle measure is shown as an example.
   a. an angle of 34°
   b. the angle closest to 90°
   c. two angles whose sum is 196°
   d. the smallest angle
   e. the greatest angle

2. Make your own geometric drawing. Include the following angles and mark them on the drawing.
   a. one angle of 58°
   b. one right angle
   c. two angles whose sum is 145°

Store Storage

A large store has a warehouse it uses for storage. Trucks back up to the loading dock where merchandise is unloaded, sorted, and stacked in the correct area of the warehouse.

1. The large shelves in the storage area are 17 feet 8 inches apart so the forklift machines can operate between the shelves. Is that distance greater than or less than 216 inches? Explain your math reasoning.

   _____

   _____

   _____

   _____

2. The dock foreman recorded these weights of the crates unloaded from one of the trucks.

Weight of Crate (tons)
$\frac{2}{8}$, $\frac{3}{8}$, $\frac{4}{8}$, $\frac{6}{8}$, $\frac{7}{8}$, $\frac{2}{8}$, $\frac{3}{8}$, $\frac{3}{8}$, $\frac{6}{8}$, $\frac{3}{8}$, $\frac{3}{8}$, $\frac{6}{8}$

   a. Make a line plot to show the data.

   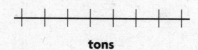

   tons

   b. The weight limit for the truck is 13,000 lb. Was the truck overweight or underweight? Explain your math reasoning.

   _____

   _____

   _____

3. The dock foreman gets to work each day at 5:30 A.M. He goes to lunch at 11:15 A.M. and gets back to work at noon. He goes home for the day at 3:05 P.M. How many hours does the foreman work in a 5-day work week?

4. In the pet supply area of the warehouse is a crate of flea shampoo for cats. Each crate holds 48 boxes. Each box holds 8 bottles of shampoo. Each bottle contains 5 mL of the chemical that gets rid of the fleas. How many liters of the chemical is in the crate of shampoo? Give your answer as a fraction and as a decimal.

Behind the Scenes

1. Most stages in professional theaters have a trap door and an elevator so large pieces of scenery or equipment can be brought to the stage. At a local theater the trap door has an area of 84 square feet, and has a whole number length and side measure. A concert grand piano needed for a performance has a length of 8 feet, 10 inches and a width of 5 feet, 2 inches. The piano fits through the trap door. What is the length and width of the trap door? What is the perimeter of the trap door? Explain your math reasoning.

_____

_____

_____

2. A play at the theater calls for a large window in the scenery. The art director has 24 feet of trim to put around the perimeter of the window. What is the greatest window area that could be made with a perimeter of 24 feet? What is the smallest possible window area? Draw models to support your conclusions.

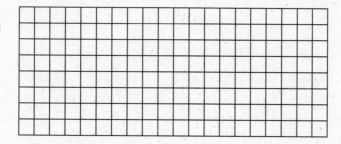

_____

_____

_____

3. At another theater, workers have to cut a new trap door. The door can be no more than 130 square feet in area, with whole-number side lengths. They have to bring in 3 items to the stage. The first item is 6 feet, 5 inches wide and 8 feet, 9 inches long. The second item is 13 feet, 4 inches wide and 7 feet, 8 inches long. The third item is 5 feet, 6 inches wide and 12 feet, 4 inches long. What size of trap door would you recommend? What is the perimeter of your trap door? Explain your math reasoning. Show your work.

_____

_____

_____

_____

Building a House

Ben the Builder is building a house for the Johnson family. He needs to use his math skills to build the house correctly.

1. Ben added to find how many drywall screws he needs to complete the house. Then he subtracted the number of screws he has to find how many screws he needs to buy. He used his calculator to help him, but then he dropped it. Now the screen looks like this.

$$
\begin{array}{r}
4\ 3\ 8\ \square \\
+\ 2\ \square\ 7\ 9 \\
\hline
\square\ 1\ \square\ 5 \\
-\ 3\ 7\ 2\ 1 \\
\hline
3\ \square\ 4\ 4
\end{array}
$$

What are the missing numbers? How many screws does Ben need to buy?
Explain your reasoning.

_____

_____

_____

_____

2. Ben will hire a crane to help the workers put the bundles of shingles on the roof. There is a limit to the weight the crane can lift at one time, but Ben wants the work done as quickly as possible. Explain to Ben what math he can use so that the crane uses the fewest lifts possible.

_____

_____

_____

3. Ben needs to choose between three brands of shingles to use on the roof. He knows he needs 89 bundles of shingles but each type of shingle weighs a different amount. He needs to take the information he has about the cost of the crane and the amount it can lift to determine the cost of using each brand.

The crane costs $350 plus an additional $150 for each hour or part of an hour the crane is used. The crane can make 4 lifts in one hour. Each lift must weigh 650 pounds or less. The weights of a bundle of each brand of shingle can be found in the table below.

Complete the table. Show your work. Then decide which brand of shingles Ben should choose. Explain your reasoning.

Shingle	Weight of each Bundle (lb)	Number of Bundles in One Lift	Number of Lifts Needed	Number of Hours Needed	Total Cost of the Crane
Brand A	75				
Brand B	80				
Brand C	85				

4. This is the floor plan of the house Ben is building.

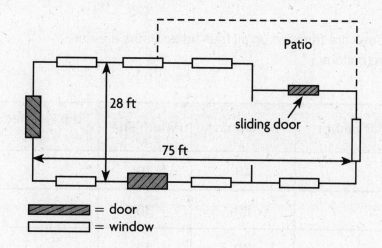

What is the estimated area of the patio? Explain your reasoning.

$A =$ _____

_____

_____

_____

_____

5. Ben needs to buy trim for around the windows and doors of the house. Complete the table to determine how much trim he should buy. Show your work.

Remember: Windows are trimmed on all four sides. Doors are not trimmed along the bottom.

Item	Number	Height (in.)	Width (in.)	Trim Needed (in.)
Window		48	40	
Door		80	36	
Sliding door		80	72	
			Total	

Party Time!

Stefan and some friends organized a party for the people in his building. The party was held at the park across the street.

1. Mr. Hoya brought 5 watermelons from his grocery store. The watermelons weighed $8\frac{1}{4}$ pounds, $9\frac{1}{4}$ pounds, $8\frac{7}{8}$ pounds, $9\frac{5}{8}$ pounds, and $10\frac{3}{4}$ pounds. At the party, 153 people each ate a $\frac{1}{4}$-pound serving of watermelon. Was the amount of leftover watermelon less than or greater than $8\frac{1}{2}$ pounds? Explain how to solve the problem. Then solve it.

_____

_____

_____

_____

2. Mr. Carlucci brought $8\frac{3}{4}$ pound pepperoni for large sandwiches. He cut the pepperoni into $\frac{1}{12}$ pound slices. A skateboarder bumped into his table and $2\frac{7}{12}$ pound of the pepperoni fell on the ground and was eaten by 3 dogs. Does Mr. Carlucci have enough pepperoni left to make 74 sandwiches if he puts one slice on each sandwich? By how much is he over or under the amount of pepperoni he needs? Show your work.

3. The Salomans offered to be in charge of drinks for the party. In addition to other beverages, they brought 4 bags of coffee that each held $2\frac{1}{2}$ pounds. When brewed, $\frac{1}{4}$ pound of coffee made 8 cups of coffee. The Salomons brewed and served 296 cups of coffee. Was any coffee left over? If so, how much coffee was left? Show your work.

4. Ramone tossed 1 quarter, 2 dimes, and 13 pennies in the wishing well at the party. What is the total amount of money as a fraction and as a decimal? Show your work.

5. At the party there were 380 places to sit, including the benches in the park and the chairs people brought to the party. Of those seats, 0.45 of them were used by women and girls. How many seats were used by men and boys? Is that fraction of the total number of seats less than or greater than $\frac{3}{5}$? Explain your mathematical thinking.

_____

_____

_____

_____

6. Some of the neighbors played a penny game. Players toss a penny in a hole and earn that number of points. Each payer tosses 3 pennies. The scores from each penny that goes in a hole are added for a final score. Is it possible to get a score of 9? If so, how could it happen?

$$8 \times \frac{5}{8} \quad \bigcirc \quad \bigcirc \quad 9 \times \frac{3}{4}$$

$$7 \times \frac{7}{8} \quad \bigcirc \quad \bigcirc \quad 8 \times \frac{1}{2}$$

$$6 \times \frac{3}{8} \quad \bigcirc \quad \bigcirc \quad 7 \times \frac{1}{4}$$

_____

_____

_____

7. Stefan and his friends used four tables for all the dishes the guests brought to the party. The tables were $2\frac{8}{10}$ meters long, 2.48 meters long, $2\frac{59}{100}$ meters long, and 2.84 meters long. Demonstrate one way to model these numbers to compare them. Write each as a decimal and order them from greatest to least using symbols.

8. One of the neighborhood apartment buildings has 8 floors. During the party, the elevator in the building was busy taking people up and down, to the party and back home. The elevator started on the ground floor. It went up $\frac{3}{8}$ of the building height, up another $\frac{2}{8}$ of the building, down $\frac{4}{8}$, up $\frac{6}{8}$, down $\frac{3}{8}$, and up $\frac{1}{8}$. What floor is the elevator on now? What move will put it back on the ground floor?

_____

_____

_____

Community Playground

James and Marvin volunteer to help build a playground in their neighborhood. Use geometry and measurement to solve each problem.

1. James sketches a design for a fence around the playground. The sketch has four points, *A, B, C, D*. It has 2 right angles, 1 obtuse angle, and 1 acute angle that measures 45°.

   a. Use a protractor to draw the design of the fence. Label the points and right angles.

   b. Name the two line segments that form the obtuse angle. Use a protractor to find the angle measure.

   _____

   c. Name the angle that forms the acute angle.

   _____

   d. Name any perpendicular lines in your sketch.

   _____

2. Marvin cuts this piece of wood along line *RT* to form the base of a birdhouse.

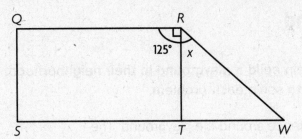

a. What is the angle measure of *x*? Write an equation to solve.

_____

_____

b. Draw a line that is parallel to line *QS* to form a line of symmetry.
   Explain how you know the base of the birdhouse has a line of symmetry.

_____

_____

c. Side *QR* measures 14 inches. Side *QS* measures 9 inches.
   Use a formula to find both the perimeter and area of the
   base of the birdhouse. Show your work.

d. Is the birdhouse base a parallelogram? Explain.

_____

_____

3. The data in the chart shows the lengths of nails Marvin uses to build his birdhouse.

Lengths of Nails (in.)						
$\frac{1}{2}$	$\frac{1}{4}$	$\frac{1}{2}$	$\frac{3}{4}$	$\frac{3}{4}$	$\frac{1}{2}$	$\frac{1}{2}$

a. Make a line plot to show the data.

b. What is the difference between the longest and shortest nails Marvin uses? Show your work.

4. James draws this diagram for a fenced-in play area. The angle shows the opening for the gate. What is the measure of the angle in degrees? Write an equation to solve.

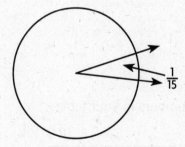

$\frac{1}{15}$

5. Marvin has 4 quarts of plant food for the flower garden.
He calculates that he needs 130 ounces to feed all of the plants.

a. Does Marvin have enough plant food? Complete the table to
solve. Explain your answer.

Quarts	_____
1	
2	
3	
4	

_____

_____

b. Describe the relationship between the numbers in your table.

_____

_____

_____

_____

Choose the correct answer.

1. The population of the United States is about 310,845,000. Which is the value of the 1 in that number?

   (A)   100,000

   (B)   1,000,000

   (C)   10,000,000

   (D) 100,000,000

2. Which number is the standard form of five million, three hundred six thousand, ninety-five?

   (A) 500,360,095

   (B)   50,306,095

   (C)   5,306,095

   (D)   5,306,950

3. A crayon factory has 3,600 crayons that need to be packaged into boxes with 40 crayons in each box. How many boxes of crayons will there be?

   (A)   9 boxes

   (B)   90 boxes

   (C) 800 boxes

   (D) 900 boxes

4. The food pantry has 1,000 cans of soup to sort. The cans are divided equally among 50 crates. How many cans are in each crate?

   (A)   20 cans

   (B)   50 cans

   (C) 200 cans

   (D) 500 cans

GO ON

5. Jenna saved 9 dollars each week for 6 weeks. Then she spent 5 dollars of the money she saved. Which expression and answer tells how much Jenna has left?

Ⓐ $6 \times (9 - 5)$; 10 dollars

Ⓑ $6 \times 9 - 5$; 49 dollars

Ⓒ $6 \times (9 - 5)$; 24 dollars

Ⓓ $6 \times 9 + 5$; 59 dollars

6. What is the value of the expression $50 \div 5 - (5 + 1)$?

Ⓐ 4

Ⓑ 6

Ⓒ 16

Ⓓ 51

7. David bought a large duffel bag for $55.96. Elena bought a smaller bag for $41.13. How much did they spend on both duffel bags?

Ⓐ $96.09

Ⓑ $96.83

Ⓒ $97.09

Ⓓ $97.90

8. Denise spent $79.98 on snow boots and $43.18 on rain boots. How much did Denise spend in all?

Ⓐ $123.16

Ⓑ $123.06

Ⓒ $123.00

Ⓓ $113.16

GO ON

9. What are the next two numbers in the pattern?

2, 8, 32, 128, _____, _____

- (A) 256, 1,024
- (B) 482, 1,928
- (C) 512, 1,024
- (D) 512, 2,048

11. Max spent $11.19 at the bakery. How much did he spend, rounded to the nearest dollar?

- (A) $12.00
- (B) $11.20
- (C) $11.10
- (D) $11.00

10. Which describes the following pattern?

1, 5, 25, 125, . . .

- (A) Add 4
- (B) Add 5
- (C) Multiply by 5
- (D) Multiply by 10

12. Brianna has 40.75 inches of ribbon for a sewing project. About how many inches of ribbon does Brianna have rounded to the nearest inch?

- (A) about 41 inches
- (B) about 40.8 inches
- (C) about 40.7 inches
- (D) about 40 inches

GO ON

Write the correct answer.

13. Mario has 78 photos that he wants
    to put in an album. The photo album
    has 13 pages. How many photos can
    Mario put on each page?

    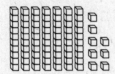

    _____

15. Mrs. Newton mails a letter that
    weighs 10.05 ounces. Write the
    word form of 10.05.

    _____

14. Gwen has $210. For how many weeks
    can Gwen spend $10 a week before
    she runs out of money?

    _____

16. What is the value of the underlined
    digit in the decimal 9.<u>4</u>8?

    _____

GO ON

17. An author signed 410 copies of his book at a special event at the book store. Decompose 410 into two factors. Use 10, 100, or 1,000 as one factor.

_____

19. Ava wants to buy a ticket for a concert. Orchestra seats cost $79.26 each, but balcony seats cost $58.48 each. How much will Ava save by buying a ticket for a balcony seat?

_____

18. An exhibit of ocean birds at the aquarium has a tank that holds 6,000 gallons of salt water. Decompose 6,000 into two factors. Use 10, 100, or 1,000 as one factor.

_____

20. Zach has $80.00 to spend on groceries. The bill comes out to $68.03. How much change does Zach get?

_____

GO ON

21. The temperatures in two U. S. cities at the same time were 54.9°F and 54.09°F. Compare the decimals. Write <, >, or =.

_____

22. Marci practiced guitar for 1.2 hours. Duane practiced piano for 1.25 hours. Compare the decimals. Write <, >, or =.

_____

23. List the operations in the correct order to find the value of the expression.

$$(10 - 5) \times 2 + 3$$

_____

24. Read and write the decimal in two other forms.

seven and thirty-eight hundredths

_____

25. Maria spent $79.05 on a dress and $9.30 on socks. How much more did she spend on the dress than on the socks?

_____

Choose the correct answer.

Use the grid for 1–4.

A company has four coffee shops in one city. The grid shows the location of each coffee shop.

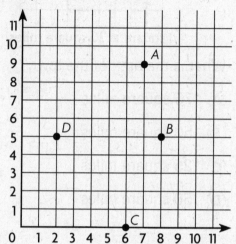

1. Which ordered pair tells the location of Coffee Shop D?

Ⓐ (2, 5)   Ⓒ (5, 5)

Ⓑ (5, 2)   Ⓓ (5, 8)

2. Which ordered pair tells the location of Coffee Shop A?

Ⓐ (7, 0)   Ⓒ (9, 7)

Ⓑ (7, 9)   Ⓓ (9, 9)

3. Which ordered pair tells the location of Coffee Shop C?

Ⓐ (0, 6)

Ⓑ (6, 0)

Ⓒ (6, 6)

Ⓓ (9, 0)

4. Which best describes how to move from Coffee Shop D to Coffee Shop B?

Ⓐ Move 8 units to the right.

Ⓑ Move 6 units up.

Ⓒ Move 6 units to the left.

Ⓓ Move 6 units to the right.

GO ON

5. The park director drew this model of a playground. Each square has an area of 6 square yards.

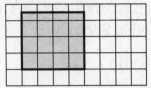

1 square = 6 square yards

What is the area of the playground?

(A) 90 square yards

(B) 84 square yards

(C) 72 square yards

(D) 48 square yards

6. Ms. Rinaldi made a model of the hallway she wants to carpet. Each square has an area of 4 square feet.

1 square = 4 square feet

What is the area of the hallway?

(A) 44 square feet

(B) 42 square feet

(C) 40 square feet

(D) 36 square feet

7. The mayor looked at this grid of his town. Each square has an area of 10 square miles.

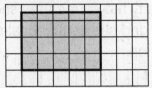

1 square = 10 square miles

What is the area of the town?

(A) 175 square miles

(B) 150 square miles

(C) 125 square miles

(D) 50 square miles

8. Juan is cutting lumber into $\frac{1}{2}$-foot lengths. How many $\frac{1}{2}$-foot lengths will he get from an 8-foot long piece of lumber?

(A) 16

(B) 8

(C) 6

(D) 4

GO ON

9. Eli has 3 cups of mixed nuts. He wants to divide it into portions that are $\frac{1}{4}$-cup each. How many portions can he make?

(A) 6

(B) 7

(C) 12

(D) 24

10. Amber has a pitcher filled with 4 cups of orange juice. She pours out $\frac{1}{2}$-cup servings until the pitcher is empty. How many $\frac{1}{2}$-cup servings does she make?

(A) 16

(B) 12

(C) 8

(D) 6

11. A store has 2 separate displays of color markers. There are 16 sets of color markers in each display. If there are 4 markers in each set, how many markers in all are on display?

(A) 32

(B) 64

(C) 128

(D) 148

12. There are 5 ballet classes at each of Dixon's Dance Studios. Each ballet class has 12 students. If there are Dixon Dance Studios in 4 different cities, how many ballet students are there in all?

(A) 240 students

(B) 200 students

(C) 120 students

(D) 60 students

GO ON

Write the correct answer.

13. A florist makes 4 different color bouquets of roses. There are 15 bouquets of each color, and one dozen roses in each bouquet. How many roses are there in all of the bouquets?

_____

15. Alex and Philip are building a play fort in their back yard. It is in the shape of this rectangular prism.

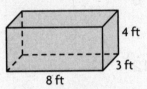

What is the area of the floor of their fort?

_____

14. Maddy is making wooden blocks to use as game cubes. Each block is a cube one inch long on each edge. The cubes will fit in the bottom layer of this game box.

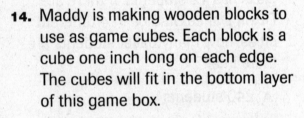

How many cubes will fit in the bottom layer of the game box?

_____

16. Mya is looking for stone tiles for the floor of a greenhouse. The greenhouse will have the dimensions of this rectangular prism.

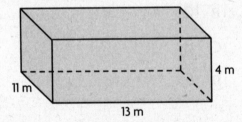

What is the floor area that Mya will need to cover with stone tiles?

_____

GO ON

17. Mr. Martin cooked some chili. His family ate $\frac{1}{3}$ of the chili for dinner. Later, as a snack, the family ate $\frac{1}{6}$ more of the chili. What part of the chili was eaten in all?

_____

19. Josh needs $\frac{2}{3}$ hour to weed a garden and $\frac{1}{12}$ hour to water the garden. What part of an hour do these two jobs take?

_____

18. In January of one winter, $\frac{3}{10}$ of a wood pile was used in a wood stove. In February, $\frac{2}{5}$ of the wood pile was used. What part of the wood pile was used up at the end of February?

_____

20. It is $\frac{3}{5}$ mile from Elaine's home to her school. It is $\frac{1}{10}$ mile from her home to the library. How much farther is Elaine's home from her school than it is from the library?

_____

GO ON

21. Jacob had $\frac{3}{4}$ of his book report left to do. He completed $\frac{3}{8}$ more of the report today. What fraction of the book report does Jacob still need to do?

_____

22. Luis played soccer for $\frac{1}{2}$ hour. Gabriella played soccer for $\frac{5}{6}$ hour. What part of an hour more did Gabriella play than Luis?

_____

23. Write the division problem $1 \div 9$ as a fraction or a mixed number.

_____

24. A group of people buys 5 pounds of corn meal to divide equally among 6 families. Write a fraction or mixed number that shows how many pounds of corn meal each family gets.

_____

25. Vanessa uses $\frac{3}{4}$ pound of flour to make a loaf of bread. To make 6 loaves, will she use more than 6 pounds of flour or less than 6 pounds of flour?

_____

Student's Name _____ Date _____

Prerequisite Skills Inventory

Item	Standard	Content Focus
1	MAFS.3.NBT.1.1	Round whole numbers.
2	MAFS.3.NBT.1.1	Add rounded numbers to find an estimate.
3	MAFS.3.NBT.1.2	Add whole numbers without regrouping.
4	MAFS.3.NBT.1.2	Add whole numbers with regrouping.
5	MAFS.3.NBT.1.1	Subtract rounded numbers to find an estimate.
6	MAFS.3.NBT.1.2	Subtract whole numbers with regrouping.
7	MAFS.3.OA.4.8	Solve multi-step word problems using models.
8	MAFS.3.MD.2.4	Interpret line plots.
9	MAFS.3.OA.1.1	Find a product using a model.
10	MAFS.3.OA.2.5	Multiply using the properties of operations.
11	MAFS.3.OA.1.3	Multiply with a factor of 6.
12	MAFS.3.OA.4.9	Identify a number pattern.
13	MAFS.3.OA.4.9	Identify and continue a number pattern.
14	MAFS.3.OA.1.4	Find a missing factor in a multiplication equation.
15	MAFS.3.NBT.1.3	Multiply by multiples of 10.
16	MAFS.3.OA.3.7	Identify an equation that is part of a set of related facts.
17	MAFS.3.OA.2.5	Divide whole numbers resulting in a quotient of 1.
18	MAFS.3.OA.3.7	Divide by 10.
19	MAFS.3.OA.3.7	Divide by 6.
20	MAFS.3.OA.3.7	Divide by 8.

Prerequisite Skills Inventory

Item	Standard	Content Focus
21	MAFS.3.OA.3.7	Divide by 8.
22	MAFS.3.OA.3.7	Divide by 9.
23	MAFS.3.NF.1.1	Divide a rectangle into two equal parts.
24	MAFS.3.NF.1.1	Identify the fraction of a model that is shaded.
25	MAFS.3.NF.1.1	Identify the fraction of a model that is shaded.
26	MAFS.3.NF.1.3d	Compare fractions with the same denominator.
27	MAFS.3.NF.1.3d	Compare fractions with the same numerator.
28	MAFS.3.NF.1.3d	Order fractions with the same denominator.
29	MAFS.3.NF.1.3b	Use a model to find an equivalent fraction.
30	MAFS.3.MD.1.1	Write a time to the closest minute given the position of the hour hand and the minute hand.
31	MAFS.3.MD.1.1	Determine elapsed time given a start time and end time.
32	MAFS.3.MD.1.1	Determine an end time given the start time and elapsed time.
33	MAFS.3.MD.1.1	Determine the relative size of one liter.
34	MAFS.3.MD.1.1	Select the most appropriate metric unit of mass.
35	MAFS.3.MD.1.1	Compare masses.
36	MAFS.3.G.A.1	Classify angles as right angles.
37	MAFS.3.G.A.1	Classify angles as right angles.
38	MAFS.3.G.A.1	Identify parallel lines.
39	MAFS.3.G.A.1	Identify a quadrilateral given a figure.
40	MAFS.3.G.A.1	Identify a quadrilateral given a description of its appearance.

Beginning-of-Year Test/Middle-of-Year Test/End-of-Year Test

Item	Lesson	Standard	Content Focus	Intervene with
1	2.8	MAFS.4.NBT.2.5	Use the properties of operations to multiply.	**R**—2.8
2	2.11	MAFS.4.NBT.2.5	Multiply a four-digit whole number by a one-digit whole number with regrouping.	**R**—2.11
3	2.4	MAFS.4.NBT.2.5	Estimate products by rounding.	**R**—2.4
4	2.7	MAFS.4.NBT.2.5	Relate a model showing partial products to a multiplication equation.	**R**—2.7
5	9.3	MAFS.4.NF.3.5	Find equivalent fractions and decimals.	**R**—9.3
6	9.1	MAFS.4.NF.3.6	Use decimal notation for fractions with denominators 10 or 100.	**R**—9.1
7	9.6	MAFS.4.NF.3.5	Add fractions in tenths to fractions in hundredths.	**R**—9.6
8	11.4	MAFS.4.MD.3.7	Determine the measure of an angle separated into parts.	**R**—11.4
9	11.2	MAFS.4.MD.3.5a	Classify an angle.	**R**—11.2
10	11.5	MAFS.4.MD.3.7	Use relationships between an angle and its parts to find an unknown.	**R**—11.5
11	11.1	MAFS.4.MD.3.5a	Relate the measure of an angle to fractional parts of a circle.	**R**—11.1
12	7.3	MAFS.4.NF.3.3d	Add fractions with like denominators.	**R**—7.3
13	7.4	MAFS.4.NF.3.3d	Subtract fractions with like denominators.	**R**—7.4
14	7.6	MAFS.4.NF.3.3b	Rename a fraction as a mixed number.	**R**—7.6
15	7.8	MAFS.4.NF.3.3c	Subtract mixed numbers with renaming.	**R**—7.8

Key: R—Reteach

Beginning-of-Year Test/Middle-of-Year Test/End-of-Year Test

Item	Lesson	Standard	Content Focus	Intervene with
16	5.3	MAFS.4.OA.2.4	Find common factors to solve a problem.	**R**—5.3
17	5.4	MAFS.4.OA.2.4	Find a common multiple to solve a problem.	**R**—5.4
18	5.5	MAFS.4.OA.2.4	Identify a prime number.	**R**—5.5
19	5.6	MAFS.4.OA.3.5	Interpret patterns with a two-operation rule.	**R**—5.6
20	12.8	MAFS.4.MD.1.1	Convert between units of time.	**R**—12.8
21	12.11	MAFS.4.MD.1.1	Recognize and apply patterns in related units of measure.	**R**—12.11
22	12.9	MAFS.4.MD.1.2	Solve a problem involving elapsed time.	**R**—12.9
23	12.10	MAFS.4.MD.1.1	Convert between mixed units of measure.	**R**—12.10
24	1.1	MAFS.4.NBT.1.1	Determine the value of a digit.	**R**—1.1
25	1.3	MAFS.4.NBT.1.2	Compare whole numbers.	**R**—1.3
26	1.6	MAFS.4.NBT.2.4	Add multi-digit whole numbers.	**R**—1.6
27	1.7	MAFS.4.NBT.2.4	Subtract multi-digit whole numbers.	**R**—1.7
28	13.4	MAFS.4.MD.1.3	Use a formula to find an unknown measure of a rectangle when given its perimeter.	**R**—13.4
29	13.1	MAFS.4.MD.1.3	Find the perimeter of a rectangle.	**R**—13.1
30	13.3	MAFS.4.MD.1.3	Find the area of combined rectangles.	**R**—13.3
31	13.5	MAFS.4.MD.1.3	Solve a real-world problem involving the area of rectangles.	**R**—13.5
32	3.2	MAFS.4.NBT.2.5	Use rounding to estimate a product.	**R**—3.2
33	3.1	MAFS.4.NBT.2.5	Multiply by tens.	**R**—3.1

Key: **R**—Reteach

Beginning-of-Year Test/Middle-of-Year Test/End-of-Year Test

Item	Lesson	Standard	Content Focus	Intervene with
34	3.7	MAFS.4.NBT.2.5	Multiply two 2-digit numbers with regrouping.	R—3.7
35	1.8A	MAFS.4.OA.1.b	Use comparative relational thinking to determine an unknown number.	R—1.8A
36	7.6	MAFS.4.NF.2.3b	Rename a fraction as a mixed number.	R—7.6
37	8.2	MAFS.4.NF.2.4b	Identify multiples of a fraction.	R—8.2
38	8.3	MAFS.4.NF.2.4b	Multiply a fraction by a whole number.	R—8.3
39	8.4	MAFS.4.NF.2.4c	Multiply a mixed number by a whole number.	R—8.4
40	4.5	MAFS.4.NBT.2.6	Use compatible numbers and basic facts to estimate a quotient.	R—4.5
41	4.3	MAFS.4.OA.1.3	Solve a problem by dividing and interpreting the remainder.	R—4.3
42	4.11	MAFS.4.NBT.2.6	Divide a multi-digit dividend by a 1-digit divisor.	R—4.11
43	4.4	MAFS.4.NBT.2.6	Use place-value relationships and basic facts to divide.	R—4.4
44	10.6	MAFS.4.G.1.3	Identify the lines of symmetry for a figure.	R—10.6
45	10.1	MAFS.4.G.1.1	Identify lines, line segments, rays, and angles.	R—10.1
46	10.4	MAFS.4.G.1.2	Identify quadrilaterals.	R—10.4
47	10.2	MAFS.4.G.1.2	Identify triangles.	R—10.2
48	6.4	MAFS.4.NF.1.1	Find a common denominator.	R—6.4
49	6.2	MAFS.4.NF.1.1	Multiply to find equivalent fractions.	R—6.2
50	6.7	MAFS.4.NF.1.2	Compare fractions with different denominators.	R—6.7

Key: R—Reteach

Student's Name _____ Date _____

Chapter 1 Test

Item	Lesson	Standard	Content Focus	Intervene with
1, 3, 4, 19	1.3	MAFS.4.NBT.1.2	Compare two multi-digit numbers.	**R**—1.3
2, 11, 16, 17	1.1	MAFS.4.NBT.1.1	Describe whole number place value relationships.	**R**—1.1
5	1.5	MAFS.4.NBT.1.1	Use place value to rename whole numbers.	**R**—1.5
6, 7	1.4	MAFS.4.NBT.1.3	Round multi-digit whole numbers.	**R**—1.4
8, 9	1.6	MAFS.4.NBT.2.4	Add multi-digit whole numbers.	**R**—1.6
10, 15, 18	1.7	MAFS.4.NBT.2.4	Subtract multi-digit whole numbers.	**R**—1.7
12	1.2	MAFS.4.NBT.1.2	Read and write multi-digit whole numbers.	**R**—1.2
13	1.8	MAFS.4.NBT.2.4	Solve comparison problems with addition and subtraction.	**R**—1.8
20	1.8A	MAFS.4.OA.1.a	Determine if an equation is true or false using comparative relational thinking.	**R**—1.8A
14	1.8A	MAFS.4.OA.1.b	Determine the unknown whole number in an equation using comparative relational thinking.	**R**—1.8A

Key: R—Reteach

Chapter 2 Test

Item	Lesson	Standard	Content Focus	Intervene with
1, 2, 7	2.10	MAFS.4.NBT.2.5	Multiply 2-digit numbers with regrouping.	**R**—2.10
3, 11, 14	2.9	MAFS.4.OA.1.3	Solve multistep multiplication problems.	**R**—2.9
4, 8	2.11	MAFS.4.NBT.2.5	Multiply 3-digit and 4-digit numbers with regrouping.	**R**—2.11
5	2.7	MAFS.4.NBT.2.5	Multiply using partial products.	**R**—2.7
6	2.1	MAFS.4.OA.1.1	Model multiplicative comparisons.	**R**—2.1
9	2.6	MAFS.4.NBT.2.5	Multiply using expanded form.	**R**—2.6
10, 13	2.8	MAFS.4.NBT.2.5	Multiply using mental math and properties.	**R**—2.8
12	2.3	MAFS.4.NBT.2.5	Multiply tens, hundreds, and thousands.	**R**—2.3
15	2.4	MAFS.4.NBT.2.5	Estimate products by rounding.	**R**—2.4
16	2.12	MAFS.4.OA.1.3	Solve multistep problems using equations.	**R**—2.12
17	2.2	MAFS.4.OA.1.2	Solve multiplicative comparison problems.	**R**—2.2
18	2.5	MAFS.4.NBT.2.5	Multiply using the Distributive Property.	**R**—2.5

Key: R—Reteach

Chapter 3 Test

Item	Lesson	Standard	Content Focus	Intervene with
1	3.1	MAFS.4.NBT.2.5	Use mental math to multiply by tens.	R—3.1
2, 5, 6	3.2	MAFS.4.NBT.2.5	Use rounding and compatible numbers to estimate products.	R—3.2
3, 4	3.1	MAFS.4.NBT.2.5	Use mental math to find products where at least one factor is a multiple of ten.	R—3.1
7, 8, 10	3.3	MAFS.4.NBT.2.5	Multiply two 2-digit numbers using area models and partial products.	R—3.3
9, 11, 12	3.4	MAFS.4.NBT.2.5	Multiply two 2-digit numbers using partial products.	R—3.4
13–15, 17	3.5	MAFS.4.NBT.2.5	Multiply two 2-digit numbers using regrouping.	R—3.5
16, 20	3.6	MAFS.4.NBT.2.5	Use strategies based on place value to compute and represent products of two 2-digit numbers in different ways.	R—3.6
18, 19, 21	3.7	MAFS.4.OA.1.3	Solve multistep word problems posed with whole numbers and having whole number answers using the four operations.	R—3.7

Key: R—Reteach

Chapter 4 Test

Item	Lesson	Standard	Content Focus	Intervene with
1, 2, 14c	4.1	MAFS.4.NBT.2.6	Use multiples to estimate quotients with up to 4-digit dividends and 1-digit divisors.	**R**—4.1
3	4.2	MAFS.4.NBT.2.6	Use models to divide whole numbers that result in remainders.	**R**—4.2
5, 6, 7	4.3	MAFS.4.OA.1.3	Interpret the remainder when solving word problems involving division of two whole numbers.	**R**—4.3
8, 9	4.4	MAFS.4.NBT.2.6	Use basic facts and place value to divide tens, hundreds, and thousands by 1-digit divisors.	**R**—4.4
10, 11	4.5	MAFS.4.NBT.2.6	Estimate quotients of two whole numbers using compatible numbers.	**R**—4.5
12	4.6	MAFS.4.NBT.2.6	Use the Distributive Property to find quotients.	**R**—4.6
13, 16	4.7	MAFS.4.NBT.2.6	Divide using repeated subtraction.	**R**—4.7
18	4.8	MAFS.4.NBT.2.6	Divide using partial quotients.	**R**—4.8
19	4.9	MAFS.4.NBT.2.6	Use base-ten blocks to model division with regrouping.	**R**—4.9
15, 20	4.10	MAFS.4.NBT.2.6	Use place value to decide where to place the first digit in a quotient.	**R**—4.10
4, 14a-b, 17	4.11	MAFS.4.NBT.2.6	Divide by 1-digit numbers.	**R**—4.11
21, 22	4.12	MAFS.4.OA.1.2	Solve multistep word problems involving division.	**R**—4.12

Key: R—Reteach

Chapter 5 Test

Item	Lesson	Standard	Content Focus	Intervene with
1, 2, 4, 10, 13, 15	5.4	MAFS.4.OA.2.4	Identify factors and multiples of a number in the range 1–100.	**R**—5.4
3	5.1	MAFS.4.OA.2.4	Use models to identify factors of a number.	**R**—5.1
5, 6	5.2	MAFS.4.OA.2.4	Use divisibility to decide if one number is a factor of another.	**R**—5.2
7–9	5.3	MAFS.4.OA.2.4	Solve word problems involving common factors.	**R**—5.3
11, 19, 20	5.6	MAFS.4.OA.3.5	Use a rule to generate a number pattern or find a certain term in the pattern.	**R**—5.6
12	5.4	MAFS.4.OA.2.4	Distinguish between factors and multiples of a number.	**R**—5.4
14	5.4	MAFS.4.OA.2.4	Solve word problems involving common multiples.	**R**—5.4
16–18, 21	5.5	MAFS.4.OA.2.4	Determine whether a number is prime or composite using its factors.	**R**—5.5

Key: R—Reteach

Chapter 6 Test

Item	Lesson	Standard	Content Focus	Intervene with
1, 8, 15	6.1	MAFS.4.NF.1.1	Determine whether fractions are equivalent.	**R**—6.1
2, 13	6.8	MAFS.4.NF.1.2	Compare and order fractions.	**R**—6.8
3, 16	6.2	MAFS.4.NF.1.1	Use multiplication to generate equivalent fractions.	**R**—6.2
4, 5	6.7	MAFS.4.NF.1.2	Compare fractions by rewriting them with a common denominator.	**R**—6.7
6, 9, 17	6.4	MAFS.4.NF.1.1	Rewrite fractions with a common denominator.	**R**—6.4
7, 11	6.3	MAFS.4.NF.1.1	Write fractions in simplest form.	**R**—6.3
10, 14	6.5	MAFS.4.NF.1.1	Find equivalent fractions to solve problems.	**R**—6.5
12, 18	6.6	MAFS.4.NF.1.2	Compare fractions using benchmarks.	**R**—6.6

Key: R—Reteach

Chapter 7 Test

Item	Lesson	Standard	Content Focus	Intervene with
1, 4, 8, 13	7.3	MAFS.4.NF.2.3d	Solve word problems involving addition of fractions having like denominators using models.	**R**—7.3
2, 12, 20	7.7	MAFS.4.NF.2.3c	Add and subtract mixed numbers with like denominators.	**R**—7.7
3, 11	7.8	MAFS.4.NF.2.3c	Subtract mixed numbers with renaming.	**R**—7.8
4, 14	7.4	MAFS.4.NF.2.3d	Solve word problems involving subtraction of fractions having like denominators using models.	**R**—7.4
5, 16, 21	7.6	MAFS.4.NF.2.3b	Rename mixed numbers as fractions greater than 1 and rename fractions greater than 1 as mixed numbers.	**R**—7.6
6	7.2	MAFS.4.NF.2.3b	Decompose a fraction into a sum of fractions with the same denominator in more than one way.	**R**—7.2
7, 15, 19	7.1	MAFS.4.NF.2.3a	Understand addition and subtraction of fractions as joining and separating parts referring to the same whole.	**R**—7.1
9	7.9	MAFS.4.NF.2.3c	Use properties of operations to add fractions with like denominators.	**R**—7.9
10	7.5	MAFS.4.NF.2.3d	Solve word problems involving addition and subtraction of fractions having like denominators using equations.	**R**—7.5
17, 18	7.10	MAFS.4.NF.2.3d	Solve multistep word problems involving addition and subtraction of fractions with the same denominator.	**R**—7.10

Key: R—Reteach

Chapter 8 Test

Item	Lesson	Standard	Content Focus	Intervene with
1, 5, 10	8.1	MAFS.4.NF.2.4a	Identify multiples of unit fractions.	R—8.1
19, 21	8.2	MAFS.4.NF.2.4b	Understand a fraction $\frac{a}{b}$ as a multiple of $\frac{1}{b}$.	R—8.2
3, 4, 6, 9, 11, 13, 14, 16, 18, 20	8.4	MAFS.4.NF.2.4c	Multiply a fraction or mixed number by a whole number.	R—8.4
7, 17	8.5	MAFS.4.NF.2.4c	Draw a diagram to solve comparison problems with fractions.	R—8.5
2, 8, 12	8.3	MAFS.4.NF.2.4b	Use a visual model to multiply a fraction by a whole number.	R—8.3

Key: R—Reteach

Chapter 9 Test

Item	Lesson	Standard	Content Focus	Intervene with
1, 5, 15	9.1	MAFS.4.NF.3.6	Use decimal notation for fractions with denominators of 10.	**R**—9.1
2, 6, 14	9.4	MAFS.4.NF.3.6	Relate fractions, decimals, and money.	**R**—9.4
3, 8	9.3	MAFS.4.NF.3.5	Express fractions with denominators of 10 and 100 as equivalent fractions and decimals.	**R**—9.3
4, 7, 10	9.5	MAFS.4.MD.1.2	Use the four operations to solve word problems involving money.	**R**—9.5
9, 18, 21	9.7	MAFS.4.NF.3.7	Compare decimals amounts.	**R**—9.7
11, 13	9.2	MAFS.4.NF.3.6	Use decimal notation for fractions with denominators of 100.	**R**—9.2
12, 16, 19	9.6	MAFS.4.NF.3.5	Add two fractions with denominators of 10 and 100.	**R**—9.6
17, 20	9.3	MAFS.4.NF.3.5	Identify or write the fraction, mixed number, or decimal shown by a visual model.	**R**—9.3

Key: R—Reteach

Chapter 10 Test

Item	Lesson	Standard	Content Focus	Intervene with
1	10.1	MAFS.4.G.1.1	Identify angles as acute, right, or obtuse.	R—10.1
2, 3, 7, 15	10.2	MAFS.4.G.1.2	Classify triangles based on the size of their angles.	R—10.2
4, 14	10.1	MAFS.4.G.1.1	Identify lines, line segments, rays, and angles.	R—10.1
5, 8, 16	10.3	MAFS.4.G.1.1	Identify lines or sides of figures as either parallel or perpendicular.	R—10.3
6, 17	10.5	MAFS.4.G.1.3	Determine whether a given two-dimensional figure has line symmetry.	R—10.5
9, 10, 19	10.4	MAFS.4.G.1.2	Recognize a quadrilateral and classify it into its appropriate subgroups.	R—10.4
11, 13, 20	10.6	MAFS.4.G.1.3	Determine the number of lines of symmetry for a given two-dimensional figure.	R—10.6
12, 18, 21	10.7	MAFS.4.G.3.5	Analyze a shape pattern to determine a missing term.	R—10.7

Key: R—Reteach

Chapter 11 Test

Item	Lesson	Standard	Content Focus	Intervene with
1, 3, 13-15	11.2	MAFS.4.MD.3.5a, MAFS.4.MD.3.5b	Relate degrees to angles and fractional parts of a circle.	**R**—11.2
2, 5, 9, 19	11.4	MAFS.4.MD.3.7	Determine the measure of an angle separated into parts.	**R**—11.4
4, 8, 16	11.1	MAFS.4.MD.3.5a	Relate angles to fractional parts of a circle.	**R**—11.1
6, 11, 17, 18	11.5	MAFS.4.MD.3.7	Draw diagrams and use equations to find unknown angle measures.	**R**—11.5
7, 10, 12, 20	11.3	MAFS.4.MD.3.6	Use a protractor to measure and draw angles.	**R**—11.3

Key: R—Reteach

Chapter 12 Test

Item	Lesson	Standard	Content Focus	Intervene with
1, 6	12.1	MAFS.4.MD.1.1	Find relative sizes of measurement units within one system of units.	R—12.1
2, 18	12.8	MAFS.4.MD.1.1	Convert between units of time.	R—12.8
3, 8	12.2	MAFS.4.MD.1.1	Convert between customary units of length.	R—12.2
4, 15	12.4	MAFS.4.MD.1.1	Convert between customary units of liquid volume.	R—12.4
5, 11	12.5	MAFS.4.MD.2.4	Make line plots to display fractional data.	R—12.5
7, 12	12.3	MAFS.4.MD.1.1	Convert between customary units of weight.	R—12.3
9, 22	12.10	MAFS.4.MD.1.2	Solve problems involving mixed units of measure.	R—12.10
10, 20	12.1, 12.11	MAFS.4.MD.1.1	Record measurement equivalents in a two-column table.	R—12.1, 12.11
13, 17	12.7	MAFS.4.MD.1.1	Solve problems involving conversion of metric units of mass and liquid volume.	R—12.7
14, 21	12.6	MAFS.4.MD.1.1	Convert between metric units of length.	R—12.6
16, 19	12.9	MAFS.4.MD.1.2	Solve real-world problems involving elapsed time.	R—12.9

Key: R—Reteach

Chapter 13 Test

Item	Lesson	Standard	Content Focus	Intervene with
1, 6, 16	13.1	MAFS.4.MD.1.3	Apply the perimeter formula for rectangles.	R—13.1
2, 9, 12, 17	13.5	MAFS.4.MD.1.3	Solve real-world problems involving the areas of rectangles.	R—13.5
3, 4, 7, 8	13.2	MAFS.4.MD.1.3	Apply the area formula for rectangles.	R—13.2
5, 13, 19	13.4	MAFS.4.MD.1.3	Find the unknown measure of a rectangle given its area or perimeter.	R—13.4
10, 15	13.1	MAFS.4.MD.1.3	Solve real-world problems involving the perimeter of rectangles.	R—13.1
11, 14, 18	13.3	MAFS.4.MD.1.3	Find the area of combined rectangles.	R—13.3

Key: R—Reteach

Getting Ready Test: Lessons 1–11

Item	Lesson	Common Error	Intervene With
1, 2	6	May not understand the place value of numbers to ten millions	**R**—GRR6
3, 4	4	May not understand how to use patterns to divide by multiples of ten	**R**—GRR4
5, 6, 23	3	May not understand how to use the order of operations to find the value of expressions	**R**—GRR3
7, 8	1	May not understand how to find sums of decimal amounts in dollars and cents	**R**—GRR1
9, 10	11	May not understand how to use multiplication to describe a pattern	**R**—GRR11
11, 12	8	May be unable to round decimals, including amounts of money, to the nearest whole number or dollar	**R**—GRR8
13, 14	5	May not understand how to use models to divide	**R**—GRR5
15, 16, 24	7	May not understand how to use place value to read, write, and represent decimals	**R**—GRR7
17, 18	10	May not be able to find the factors of multiples of 10, 100, and 1,000	**R**—GRR10
19, 20, 25	2	May not understand how to find differences of decimal amounts in dollars and cents	**R**—GRR2
21, 22	9	May not understand how to use place value to compare decimals	**R**—GRR9

Key: R—Reteach

Getting Ready Test: Lessons 12–20

Item	Lesson	Common Error	Intervene With
1–4	17	May not understand how to use ordered pairs to locate points on a grid	**R**—GRR17
5–7	18	May not understand how use tiling to find the area of a rectangle	**R**—GRR18
8–10	15	May not understand how to use repeated subtraction to solve problems involving division with fractions	**R**—GRR15
11–13	19	May not understand how to find the product of three factors	**R**—GRR19
14–16	20	May not understand how to find the area of the base of a rectangular prism	**R**—GRR20
17–19	12	May not know how to add fractions when one denominator is a multiple of the other	**R**—GRR12
20–22	13	May not know how to add fractions when one denominator is a multiple of the other	**R**—GRR13
23–24	16	May not understand how to write division problems as fractions	**R**—GRR16
25	14	May not understand how to compare the size of the product to the size of each factor when multiplying fractions	**R**—GRR14

Key: R—Reteach